FASHION AND TEXTILE INFORMATION DIRECTORY

2000-2001

A Directory for artists, designers, lecturers, teachers, craftsmen, students, fashion and textile enthusiasts

PUBLISHED BY FATEC
FASHION & TEXTILE EDUCATIONAL CONSULTANCY
PO Box 26, Boston, Lincolnshire PE21 9BL
Tel/Fax: 01205 355360

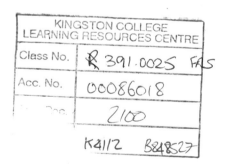

ISBN   0 9533285 11

FASHION AND TEXTILE SUPPLIERS DIRECTORY

Published by FATEC

FASHION & TEXTILE EDUCATIONAL CONSULTANCY

Personally researched by:
The Fashion and Textile Education Consultancy
PO Box 26,
Boston
Lincolnshire UK
PE21 9BL
Tel/Fax: 01205 355360

Pub. 1998 The Fashion & Textile Suppliers' Directory 1999

Pub. 1999 The Fashion and Textile Information Directory 2000/2001
(incorporating The Fashion and Textile Suppliers' Directory).

The Fashion and Textile Information Directory 2000/2001 is the 2nd edition
of this annual publication. Each year FATEC contacts all companies listed requesting
full up-to-date information relating to their business, for inclusion in the latest Directory.

FATEC would like to thank all companies for taking time to
complete the information details and for their continued support and interest in the Directory.

Do you want to be included in the next edition of: The Fashion and Textile Information Directory?

Each year the Directory is fully up-dated providing opportunities
for the inclusion of new entries from

- Suppliers'

- Guilds/Societies/Associations

- Museums and Research Centres

- Supplementary Information

Please contact FATEC giving details listing:

Organisation ....

Address...

....

....

Tel ....Fax...

Contact Name ....

Please note all entries are included at the editors discretion.

We are dependent upon businesses keeping us up-dated of any changes throughout the year.
In this way keeping FATEC up-to-date on any new developments

FASHION AND TEXTILE INFORMATION DIRECTORY

2000-2001

Published by FATEC
FASHION & TEXTILE EDUCATIONAL CONSULTANCY

Welcome to the second edition of the Fashion and Textile Information Directory, an easy to use reference index, providing valuable information and references relating to the Fashion & Textile Industry. This Directory gives quick and easy access to suppliers with details listing: books, periodicals, beads, buttons, fabric, fashion forecasting, embroidery, millinery, ribbons and trimmings, printing suppliers, knitting, yarns, weaving, restoration and conservation products and equipment, suppliers and specialists.

This publication contains a wealth of information listing over 1000 entries, acting as a valuable source of reference listing Suppliers and information relating to specialist Guilds, Societies and Associations. Museums and Research Centres are detailed featuring many of the best collections of costume, fashion and textiles in the United Kingdom, however having international readership.

Companies listed range from manufacturers, distributors and retailers. Some companies deal solely with trade, others with educational establishments, however the majority of companies deal in small minimum orders, providing excellent service to anyone requiring small supplies for collections, project work, small business runs etc.

All entries are listed alphabetically by name in the appropriate section and in the Company Index starting on page 187 giving details, contact addresses etc. This publication is a necessity for anyone who is interested in the world of fashion and textiles. It is aimed at designers, businesses, lecturers, teachers, students, researchers and fashion and textile enthusiaists etc.

If you are interested in a particular company, it is advisable to contact, prior to visiting, checking out opening times to avoid any disappointment. Many of the businesses listed deal solely with with mail order, providing fast mail order delivery.

Please contact FATEC, with any comments or suggestions for future editions of the Directory or if you would like to see any further information or references included that would be useful to others.

Carol M. Brown

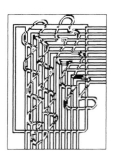 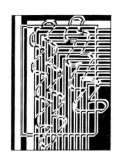 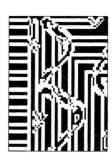 

ANNETTE CLARKE

Amber beads - chips, ovals, facets, discs, spheres, natural shapes, assorted colours. Amber cabochons, freshwater pearls - varied colours. Gemstone beads, cabochons, fossils etc. Mail order only.

Annette Clarke. 202 Swanshurst Lane, Moseley, Birmingham B13 0AW
Tel/Fax: 0121 778 6314

BALLOU FINDINGS LTD

Wide range of carat gold, gold filled, sterling silver and metal jewellery findings. No order too small.

Ballou Findings Ltd. 15 Cochran Close, Crownhill, Milton Keynes MK8 0AJ
Tel: 01908 569311 Fax: 01908 260262

BEADS

Rare, antique, precious, ethnic loose beads, pendants, threads, and fasteners. Beadwork and jewellery specialist for stringing and repairs. Tuition and books available. Retail only, no mail order.

Beads. 259 Potobello Road, London W11 1LR
Tel/Fax: 020 7792 3436

BEADBOX LTD

The bead lover's collection is a mail order catalogue supplying a variety of beads, books, tools and accessories that will appeal to the dedicated beader.

Beadbox Ltd. 67 Askew Road, London W12 9AH
Tel: 020 8740 8770 Fax: 020 8740 4473

BEAD EXCLUSIVE

Mail order company. Manufacturer of ranges of bead jewellery and 1000's of beads and components from all over the world. Full colour catalogue available.

Bead Exclusive. 4 Samara Park, Cavalier Road, Heathfield,
Newton Abbott TQ12 6TR
Tel: 01626 834934 Fax: 01626 834787

THE BEAD SHOP

Retail and wholesale beads, findings and associated products. Over 400 lines of beads in all materials, findings, kits, threads, thonging and books. Mail order catalogue available.

The Bead Shop. 21A Tower Street, Covent Garden, London WC2H 9NS
Tel: 020 7240 0931 Catalogue enquiries: 020 8553 3240

BRIGHT DESIGNS

Handmade beads

Bright Designs. 9 Penylan Lane, Oswestry, Shropshire SY11 2AQ

THE BRIGHTON BEAD SHOP

A cosmopolitan range of beads, pendants, findings and threads in a wide range of materials, shapes and sizes. Wholesale, retail and trade. Same day mail order service. Large 72 page full colour catalogue available.

The Brighton Bead Shop. Dept. FT, 21 Sydney Street, Brighton, East Sussex BN1 4EN
Tel: 01273 675077 Fax: 01273 692803

BURHOUSE LTD

Wholesale distributors. Jewellery components and gemstones. 10,000 stock lines. Catalogue available. Visits by appointment.

Burhouse Ltd. Quarmby Mills, Tanyard Road, Oakes, Huddersfield HD3 4YP
Tel: 01484 655675 Fax: 01484 460036

CHARISMA (BEADWORK SUPPLIES)

Wide range of embroidery beads, rocaille or seed beads, metallic, pearl, dellicia loomwork beads, bugles, looms, needles, threads, findings and accessories and books.
Mail order catalogue available £2.50 cheque or postal order.

Charisma. 16 Station Road, Oakley, Bedfordshire MK43 7RB
Tel: 01234 822505

CONSTELLATION

Importers, wholesalers and a mail order company selling loose beads from around the world: seahorses, shells, moons, stars, gemclips, rocailles, bugles etc. Jewellery fittings, tools, threads and wires. Send 8 x 1st class stamps for a full colour catalogue.

Constellation. P O Box 109, Crewe CW2 7FF
Tel/Fax: 01270 251803

CRAFT DEPOT

Over 7000 craft items at retail and wholesale prices. A large selection of beads available. Catalogue Ê4.00 refundable when spending Ê20.00 or more. Exclusively mail order.

Craft Depot. Somerton Park, Somerton, Somerset TA11 6SB
Tel: 01458 274727 Fax: 01458 272932

CRAFTY THINGS

Importers of jewellery mountings, findings, pendants, accessories and charms for the craft industry. Mail order only.

Crafty Things. 130 Southampton Road, Lymington, Hampshire SO41 8NA
Tel: 01590 677328 Fax: 01590 616294

CREATIVE BEADCRAFT LIMITED

Importers and distributors of beads, imitation pearls, jewellery findings, trimmings, sequins, feathers, imitation stones etc.

Creative Beadcraft Ltd. Denmark Works, Beamond End, Amersham, Buckinghamshire HP7 ORX
Tel: 01494 715606 Fax: 01494 718510

DAISY CHAINS

Jewellery making components and beads etc. Mail order only.
Catalogue available - 3 x 1st class stamps.
Daisy Chains. The Twll, Kerry, Newtown, Powys SY16 4LU
Tel: 01686 670495

DELICATE STITCHES

Beads, sequins, crystals, silk ribbons, embroidery threads, fine fabrics and books.
Delicate Stitches. 339 Kentish Town Road, Kentish Town, London NW5 2TJ
Tel: 020 7267 9403 Fax: 020 7284 2062

EARRING THINGS - THE BEAD MERCHANT

A wide range of beautiful beads, jewellery making supplies, cabochons, findings, tools and project books etc. available retail, mail order and wholesale. Please phone for catalogue details. Mail order, shop/showroom.
Earring Things. Craft Workshops, South Pier Road, Ellesmere Port, South Wirral L65 4FW
Tel: 0151 356 4444 Fax: 0151 355 3377

ELLIS AND FARRIER

Beads, sequins, diamante, sequin and lurex braids, imitation pearls, jewellery findings, feathers etc.
Ellis and Farrier. Denmark Works, Beamond End, Amersham, Buckinghamshire HP7 ORX
Tel: 01494 715606 Fax: 0151 355 3377

ELLS BELLS LTD

Sequins, stars, beads: bugle, clear, coloured, pearl etc. Findings and kits.
Ells Bells Ltd. Unit 15, Mead Business Centre, Mead Lane, Hertford, Hertfordshire SG13 7BJ
Tel: 01992 582712 Fax: 01992 505439

GROSVENOR STONES LTD

Semi precious beads: Amber, freshwater pearls, blister and cultured pearls, plus a select range of precious stone beads. Send 4 x 1st class stamps for brochure. Mail order service. Minimum order 30 strings, any assortment.
Grosvenor Stones Ltd. 329 Chiswick High Road, London W4 4HS
Tel: 020 8995 1802 Fax: 020 8995 6976

HARLEQUIN

Handmade Polymer clay beads and buttons in any colour, shape or size.
Mail order catalogue available.
Harlequin. 2 Elvin Crescent, Rottingdean, Brighton, East Sussex BN2 7FF
Tel: 01273 306130 Fax: 01273 306130

HARLEQUIN OF ENGLAND

Covered buttons and belts.
Harlequin of England. Manningtree, Essex CO11 1UX
Tel: 01206 396167(24 hrs)

HOMECRAFT

Embroidery seed beads, beadwork starter packs and other needlecraft products.
Mail order only.

Homecraft. 16 Crescent Parade, Uxbridge Road, Uxbridge, Middlesex UB10 0LG
Tel: 01895 238152 Fax: 01895 847954

INTERNATIONAL CRAFT

Glass, ceramic, pearl, wood, semi precious stones and beads, jewellery findings.
Catalogue available.

International Craft. 47a Berwick Street, London W1V 3RA
Tel/Fax: 020 7437 5184

KALA EMPORIUM LTD

Beads, sequins, rhinestones, mirrors, braids and tassels. Specialising in beaded fringing from 3" to 18" used in line dancing.

Kala Emporium Ltd. 134 Station Street West, Coventry CV6 5ND
Tel: 024 7668 6457 Fax: 024 7663 7057

KALEIDOSCOPE

Beads, stones, cabochons and jewellery findings. Over 5000 different items available.
Retail, wholesale and mail order.

Kaleidoscope. 3 Grove Park, Brislington, Bristol BS4 3LG
Tel: 0117 971 5768 Fax: 0117 972 3739

KERNOWCRAFT ROCKS & GEMS LTD

Gemstones, jewellery findings, beads, tools, jewellery making supplies etc.
Free colour catalogue available.

Kernowcraft Rocks and Gems Ltd. Bolingey, Perranporth, Cornwall TR6 0DH
Tel: 01872 573888 Fax: 01872 573704

THE LONDON BEAD COMPANY

Beads, sequins, crystals, silk ribbons, embroidery threads, fine fabrics and books.
Mail order catalogue available.

The London Bead Company. 339 Kentish Town Road, Kentish Town, London NW5 2TJ
Tel: 020 7267 9403 Fax: 020 7284 2062

MAGPIE LAPIDARY & MINERALS

Beads and findings. Rocks, minerals, fossils and lapidary supplies.

Magpie Lapidary & Minerals. 25 High Street East, Uppingham, Rutland LE15 9PY
Tel: 01572 823294

MANCHESTER MINERALS

One of Europe's leading specialist suppliers of lapidary and jewellery making tools and equipment, gemstones, findings and natural crystals. 176 page colour catalogue.

Manchester Minerals. Stockport, Cheshire SK4 1DP
Tel: 0161 477 0435 Fax: 0161 480 5095

MINERAL CRAFT NORTH

Cabochons, polished stones, jewellery components etc.

Mineral Craft North. 19-21 Sunlane, Wakefield WF1 1JD

M. J. J. TRIMCRAFT

Educational suppliers to art and craft sections. Sequins, beads, buttons, ribbons and trimmings.

M.J.J. Trimcraft. Trimcraft House, 100 Spring Hall lane, Halifax HX1 4TW
Tel: 01422 381723 Fax: 01422 381725

NECKLACE MAKER WORKSHOP

Exotic beads: rare, precious, antique, handmade, collectables, loose beads, threads and fasteners available. Unrepeatable job lots. Commissions, sale or hire. NB. No mail order.

Necklace Maker Workshop. 259 Portabello Road, London W11 1LR
Tel/Fax: 020 7792 3436

THE NORTHERN BEAD COMPANY

Beautiful beads from all corners of the world: glass, wood, metal ceramic, semi-precious beads, cabochons, jewellery findings, wires, thonging, beading needles, jewellery pliers, bead looms and accessories. Catalogue available.

The Northern Bead Company. 36A Barkston House, Croyden Street, Leeds LS11 9RT
Tel/Fax: 0113 244 3033

PINFLAIR t/a ELLS BELLS LTD

Sequins, stars, beads: bugle, clear, coloured, pearl etc. Findings and kits.

Ells Bells Ltd. Unit 15, Mead Business Centre, Mead Lane, Hertford, Hertfordshire SG13 7BJ
Tel: 01992 582712 Fax: 01992 505439

PHOENIX CRAFTS

Delicia loomwork beads, seed and miniature and bugle beads, Nymo thread in a range of colours, needles, findings etc.

Phoenix Crafts. 25 Churchyard, Hitchin, Hertfordshire SG4 1HP

P J MINERALS

Supplier of beads, gemstones, artificial stones, accessories and jewellery findings imported from worldwide sources.

P J Minerals. Liverpool Road, Ainsdale, Southport, Merseyside PR8 3LT

THE ROCKING RABBIT TRADING COMPANY

Range of beads, jewellery findings. Mail order, full colour catalogue available showing hundreds of beads in many shapes, materials and designs.

The Rocking Rabbit Trading Company. 135 Cambridge Road, Milton, Cambridge CB4 6BD
Tel: 0870 606 1388 Fax: 01954 252128

SEWING SEEDS

3-cut and fancy seed beads. Mail order only.

Sewing Seeds. 38 Elmore House, Minet Road, London SW9 7TH
Tel/Fax: 020 7737 1543

SPANGLES

Mail order, retail and wholesale. Beads, beading equipment and beading books. Retail lacemaking bobbins.

Spangles. 1 Casburn Lane, Burwell, Cambridge CB5 0ED
Tel/Fax: 01638 742024

SPELLBOUND BEAD COMPANY

Importers and retailers of over 2,000 different lines of beads and findings. Retail and wholesale.

Spellbound Bead Company. 45 Tamworth Street, Lichfield, Staffordshire WS13 6JW
Tel: 01543 417650 Fax: 019922 867682

THE STONE CORNER

Jewellery components, cut stones, beads, crystals, fossils and stones cut in a wide variety of materials available in retail outlet. Mail order service available.

The Stone Corner. 42A High Street, Old Town, Hastings, East Sussex TN34 3ER
Tel: 01424 431318 Fax: 01424 439915

TELFORDS

Mail order suppliers of craft materials, specialising in bead packs.

Telfords. 25 Orpington Road, Winchmore Hill, London N21 3PD
Tel: 020 8882 7729

THE TRIMMINGS COMPANY

Top fashion trimmings for manufacturers. Products include: haberdashery, trimmings, beads, braids, diamante, lace, sequins etc.

The Trimmings Company. 5 Harp Business Centre, Apsley Way, London NW2 7LU
Tel: 020 8208 4200

Remember to mention the **FASHION & TEXTILE INFORMATION DIRECTORY** *When ordering your supplies*

FATEC
FASHION
AND
TEXTILE
EDUCATIONAL
CONSULTANCY

AMERICAN CRAFT BOOKS

Craft publications from the USA. Colour catalogue available.

American Craft Books. 154 Devon Road, Luton, Bedfordshire LU2 0RL

AUSTRALIAN FOLK ART BOOKS

A wide range of over 100 books, pattern packs and videos in both traditional and decorative styles for beginners and advanced level painters.

Australian Folk Art Books. 8 Easton Hill, Easton, Nr Newbury, Berkshire RG20 8ED
Tel: 01488 608427 Fax: 01488 657757

AVRIL WHITTLE BOOKSELLER

Specialist in scarce and out-of-print books by mail order. All aspects of textiles, art, crafts, design, costume, fashion, lace, weaving, etc. Catalogues issued (free!).
Search service (registration fee £2.50)

Avril Whittle Bookseller. Swarthgill House, Garsdale, Sedbergh, Cumbria LA10 5PD
Tel: 015396 20026 Fax: 015396 21770

BARNABY'S CRAFT BOOKS

Specialists in craft and interior design books. Mail order service. Trade enquiries welcome.

Barnaby's Craft Books. 173 Windsor Road, Ilford, Essex 1G1 1HE
Tel: 020 8553 9970 Fax: 020 8220 6527

B. T. BATSFORD LTD

Publishers of fashion, textile, design and history of costume books.
Books can be ordered by mail order.

B.T. Batsford Ltd. 10 Bleinheim Court, Brewery Road, London N7 9NJ
Tel: 020 7700 7611 Fax: 020 7700 7742

BENJAMIN DENT & COMPANY LTD

Fashion and textile publications.

Benjamin Dent & Company Ltd. Head Office: 23 Bloomsbury Square, London WC1A 2PJ
Tel: 020 7637 2211 Fax: 020 7637 2248

BLACK CAT BOOKS

Specialist bookseller of antiquarian second hand and out-of- print books on textiles, needlework, costume, fashion, womens magazines 1750 - 1950 including Vogue. New books also available to order. Catalogues issued quarterly. Visitors welcome by appointment.

Black Cat Books. Meadow Cottage, High Road, Wortwell, Harleston, Norfolk. IP20 0EN
Tel: 01986 788826

BOOKS BY POST LTD

Needlecrafts and design books by mail order.

Books By Post Ltd. 2 Church Lane, East Aldershot GU11 3BT
Tel: 01252 331722

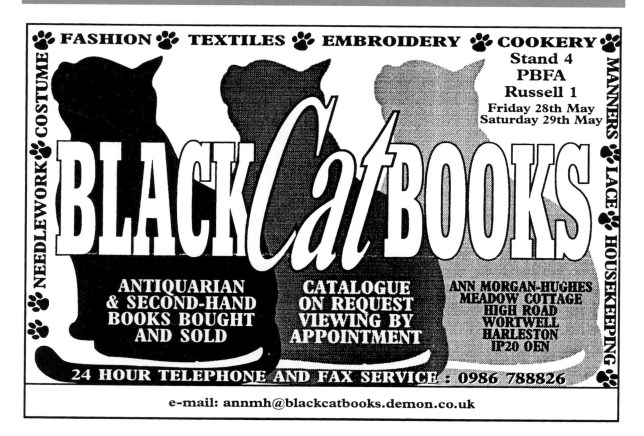

BOOKS TO ORDER

From calligraphy to sewing to crochet. Catalogue available.

Books-to-Order. Freepost, Marlborough, Wiltshire SN8 1YZ
Tel: 01672 516789

BOWDON BOOKS

Secondhand books on textile arts bought and sold in general shop. Specialist room with over 1000 textile arts books. Mail order available.

Bowdon Books. 33 Lowergate, Clitheroe, Lancashire BB7 1AD
Tel: 01200 425333

THE DOVER BOOKSHOP

Sellers of copyright free images, design and supporting visual references. A wide range of illustrative design books. Full mail order, free catalogue available.

The Dover Bookshop. 18 Earlham Street, London WC2H 9LN
Tel: 020 7836 2111 Fax: 020 7836 1603 (24 hour line)

BUTTERICK COMPANY LTD

Extensive range of sewing related books and educational resource packs, Butterick, Vogue and See and Sew paper pattern ranges for homesewers and dressmakers.

Butterick Company Ltd. New Lane, Havant, Hampshire PO9 2ND
Tel: 01705 486221 Fax: 01705 492769

D & J YOUNG

Textile arts, needlecrafts, costume, fashion, lace, weaving and knitting sold by mail order and at fairs. Catalogues issued.

D & J Young. Fairview Cottage, Groes, Llwyd, Welshpool SY21 9BZ
Tel: 01938 55149

EASTMAN MACHINE COMPANY LTD

Books for the apparel industry

Eastman Machine Company Ltd. Duro House, Station Estate, Eastwood Close, London E18 1BY
Tel: 020 8989 7784

EMBROIDERERS' GUILD BOOKSHOP

The Guild stocks an excellent range of embroidery and textile books.
A popular mail order service is available.

Embroiderers' Guild. Apartment 41, Hampton Court Palace, Surrey KT8 9AU
Tel: 020 8943 1229 Fax: 020 8977 255730

FATEC - FASHION & TEXTILE EDUCATIONAL CONSULTANCY

Promotes and supports the development of fashion and textiles in education.
Publisher of the Fashion & Textile Suppliers' Directory and teaching aids.

FATEC. PO Box 26, Boston, Lincolnshire PE21 9BL
Tel/Fax: 01205 355360

FELICITY WARNES

Specialist bookseller - antiquarian, second hand and out-of-print books on fashion, tailoring, costume, accessories, lace, embroidery, knitting, textiles and social history..

Felicity J. Warnes. The Old Bookshop, 36 Gordon Road, Enfield, Middlesex EN2 0PZ
Tel: 020 8367 1661 Fax: 020 8372 1035

R . D. FRANKS LTD.

Superb range of fashion and textile periodicals and books. Table top equipment, tailors models, mail order available all around the world. Shop opening times Mon - Fri 9 am - 5 pm

R. D. Franks Ltd. Kent House, Market Place (off Titchfield Lane), Oxford Circus, London WIN 8EJ
Tel: 020 7636 1244 Fax: 020 7436 4904

GUILD OF MASTER CRAFTSMAN PUBLICATIONS LTD

Castle Place, 166 High Street, Lewes, East Sussex BN7 1XU

ITBD PUBLICATIONS

Fashion and textile publications: International Textiles, International Colour Authority, Interior, Beachwear and Skinwear, Fashion - Forecast International etc.

ITBD Publications. 23 Bloomsbury Square, London WC1A 2PJ
Tel: 020 7637 2211 Fax: 020 7637 2248

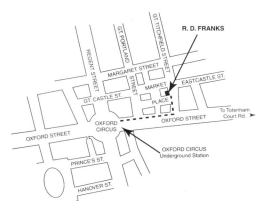

JENIFER FROST

Antiquarian and secondhand books on embroidery, lace, needlework, knitting, crochet and design. Mail order.

Jenifer Frost. 134 West Pottergate, Norwich NR2 4BW
Tel/Fax: 01603 611051

JOHN IVES BOOKSELLER

Mail order service worldwide of scarce and out-of-print books on the history of needlework, textile, costume, embroidery and fashion. Scarce and out-of-print books on embroidery, needlework, lace, history of costume, fashion and textiles etc. Free search service for out-of-print books on these subjects.

John Ives Bookseller. 5 Normanhurst Drive, St. Margarets, Twickenham, Middlesex TW1 1NA
Tel: 020 8892 6265

JOURNAL FOR SPINNERS, WEAVERS AND DYERS

Quarterly magazine of the Association of Guilds for Weavers, Spinners and Dyers, containing articles on the three disciplines and related textile crafts, to encourage, inspire, and educate all who are interested in textiles.

Journal of Spinners, Weavers and Dyers. Setters Globe, Brewery Lane, Holcombe, Bath BA3 5EG
Tel: 01761 233001

JUDITH MANSFIELD BOOKS

Secondhand and out-of-print books, magazines and ephemera.
Book room open for viewing, by appointment.

Judith Mansfield Books. Claremount South, Burnley Road, Todmordon, Lancashire OL14 5LH
Tel/Fax: 01706 816487

KEITH SMITH BOOKS

General secondhand bookseller, specialising in books on needlecraft, textiles and rugmaking, fashion and costumes. Regular catalogues available. Booksearch available. Shop open Mon - Sat 10am - 5pm.

Keith Smith Books. 78B, The Homend, Ledbury, Herefordshire HR8 1BX
Tel: 01531 635336

LESLEY JONES

Period patterns, books and publications on embroidery, crochet, knitting and needlecrafts.

Lesley Jones. 23 Gadesden Road, West Ewell, Epsom, Surrey KT19 9LB
Tel: 0181 394 2431

SACKETTS BOOKS ON WEAVING & TEXTILES

Mail order book service, specialising in out-of-print, old and rare books for weavers, spinners, dyers, fabric printers and textile artists. Send 1st class stamp for catalogue.

Sacketts Books on Weaving & Textiles. Rose Cottage, Higher Chillington, Ilminster, Somerset TA19 OPT
Tel/Fax: 01460 30105

S. B. BOOKS

Needlework books to your door. Dressmaking, tailoring, patchwork, quilting, lacemaking, soft furnishing, embroidery, cross stitch etc. Mail order lists available.

S. B. Books. PO Box 30, Market Drayton, Shropshire TF9 3ZZ
Tel: 01630 658156 Fax: 01630 653181

SEARCH PRESS LTD

Search Press Ltd publish a range of full colour books on art, crafts, textile crafts, and needlecrafts, operating a mail order service. Please ring for a complete catalogue.

Search Press Ltd. Wellwood, North Farm Road, Tunbridge Wells, Kent TN2 3DR
Tel: 01892 510850 Fax: 01892 515903

SLIPKNOT

The journal of the Knitting and Crochet Guild - "Preserving the best of the old while exploring the new" for handknitters, machine knitters and crocheters.

Slipknot. The Knitting and Crochet Guild. 228 Chester Road North, Kidderminster, Worcestershire DY10 1TH
Tel: 01562 754367

TEXTILE CRAFT BOOKS

Embroidery, needlework, patchwork and quilting books.

Textile Craft Books. 129 Station Road, Cark-in-Cartmel, Grange-over-Sands, Cumbria LA11 7NY
Tel/Fax: 015395 59009

THE TEXTILE INSTITUTE PUBLICATIONS

Textile Titles of the World - The Textile Institute's catalogue includes over 400 titles in 20 different textile areas.

The Textile Institute. 10 Blackfriars Street, Manchester M3 5DR
Tel: 0161 834 8457 Fax: 0161 835 3087

THAMES & HUDSON LTD

Book publisher - subject areas include art, photography, costume, fashion, textiles, design, architecture, archaeology, CD Roms. Catalogue available.

Thames & Hudson Ltd. 181A Holborn Place, London WC1V 7QX
Tel: 020 7845 5000 Fax: 020 7845 5050

TRAPLET PUBLICATIONS LTD

Full range of books and videos.

Traplet Publications Ltd. Traplet House, Severn Drive, Upton-upon-Severn, Worcestershire WR8 0JL
Tel: 01684 594505 Fax: 01684 594586

WELL HEAD BOOKS

Specialist supplier of needlecraft, fashion and textile books. Wholesale and retail supplies.

Well Head Books. The Old Vicarage, Bourton, Gillingham, Dorset SP8 5BJ
Tel: 01747 840213 Fax: 01747 840724

WINDSOR BOOKS INTERNATIONAL

Book distributors for art, embroidery and needlecrafts publications.

Windsor Books International. The Boundary, Wheatley Road, Garsington, Oxford OX44 9EJ
Tel: 01865 361122 Fax: 01865 361133

BUTTON & BELT SERVICES LTD

Manufacturers of covered buttons and belts, sale of associated machinery and components. Buttons and belts covered in customers' fabrics.

Button & Belt Services Ltd. 15 Glebe Road, Stanmore, Middlesex HA7 4EJ
Tel: 020 8954 8371 Fax: 020 8954 8371

BUTTON COVERING SERVICE

Button covering service covering buttons for dressmaking, bridalwear, soft furnishing and upholstery in clients own fabrics. Many sizes available. Quick postal service.

Button Covering Service. PO Box 2, 24, Venton Road, Falmouth, Cornwall TR11 4JX
Tel/Fax: 01326 314448

BUTTON DIRECT LTD

Button manufacturer and suppliers to the clothing industry. Buttons dyed to match your fabrics. Cloth-covered buttons manufactured.

Button Direct Ltd. Unit 2A, Ada Street Workshops, 8 Andrews Road, Hackney, London E8 4QN
Tel: 020 7249 3900 Fax: 07070 760534

THE BUTTON LADY

Suppliers of Norwegian pewter clasps, buttons and handmade buttons from natural materials, also a large range of novelty "American" shapes, slipper soles and 3 mm doll buttons. Agent for Cash's labels and address labels.

The Button Lady. 16 Hollyfield Road South, Sutton Coldfield, West Midlands B76 1NX
Tel: 0121 329 3234

THE BUTTON QUEEN

The button speciality. Extensive range of antique and modern buttons, diamante, mother of pearl, glass, decorative, men's tailoring buttons, blazer buttons and button covering service available.

The Button Queen. 19 Marylebone Lane, London W1M 5FE
Tel/Fax: 020 7935 1505

THE BUTTON WORKSHOP

Button covering service in selected fabric. The Button Workshop provides a mail order service using high quality Astor buttons.

The Button Workshop. 25 Whitmore Lane, Sunningdale, Ascot, Berkshire SL5 0NS
Tel/Fax: 01344 872367

DUTTONS FOR BUTTONS

10,000 buttons. International selection 1930's-1999. Glass, metal, mother of pearl, "Swarovoski" - also haberdashery and needlecrafts: buttons, elastics, lace and trimmings, sewing threads and fastenings. Everything for sewing. A division of Goodmans and Sons. Branches at Harrogate, York, Ilkley, Keighley and Leeds.

Duttons for Buttons. 3 Church Street, Ilkley, West Yorkshire LS29 9DR
Tel: 01943 601850 Fax: 01943 603137

The Button Workshop

Offers the couture designer/dressmaker a fast and efficient button covering service in your own fabric, using high quality ASTROR° buttons...

- buttons for wedding dresses, bridesmaids dresses and waistcoats
- buttons for suits, dresses and jackets
- styles: dome, highball and double
- no quantity too small

small sizes only 20p
postage & packing 75p

Ring/fax 01344 872367
25 Whitmore Lane, Sunningdale, Ascot Berkshire SL5 0NS

FRAMECRAFT MINIATURES LTD

Manufacturers and distributors of over 300 products for craft and needlework designs. Ceramic buttons by Mill Hill available. Mail order catalogue, send 4 x 1st class stamps.

Framecraft Miniatures Ltd. 372-376 Summer Lane, Hockley, Birmingham, West Midlands B19 3QA
Tel: 0121 212 0551

CMP HAMBICO LTD

Button supplier, haberdashery and trimmings.

CMP Hambico Ltd. Units B4 - 5, Wellington Road Industrial Estate, Leeds LS12 2UA
Tel: 0113 244 9810 Fax: 0113 242 5077

HARLEQUIN

Covered buttons made in your own fabric, all handmade for the individual. Full colour brochure showing full range of products.

Harlequin. Riverside Avenue, Manningtree, Essex C011 1UX
Tel: 01206 396167 Fax: 01206 397008

IMPEX CREATIVE CRAFTS LTD

Haberdashery, trimmings, pom poms, buttons, rhinestones, sequins etc.

Impex Creative Crafts Ltd. Impex House, Atlas Road, Wembley, Middlesex HA9 0TX
Tel: 020 8900 0999 Fax: 020 8900 1101

JOHN COLLIER BUTTONS LTD

Haberdashery, braids, buckles, bias binding, buttons etc.

John Collier Buttons Ltd. 79-80 Margaret Street, London W1N 7HB
Tel: 020 7636 2302 Fax: 020 7255 1446

J. V. LANDERS

Machine and hand pleating covered buttons made from own selected material. Knife and box pleating, accordian, sunray, antique and crystal pleating. Mail order service and special rates available.

J. V. Landers. 6 Stone Bridge Centre, Rangemoor Road, London N15
Tel/Fax: 020 8808 0066

POLDY LTD

Button covering machinery.

Poldy Ltd. Unit 19, Hallmark Trading Centre, Fourth Way, Wembley, Middlesex HA9 0LB
Tel: 020 8795 5007

POLYOPOLY

Specialises in custom made buttons to match customer's swatch. Mail order. Visits by appointment.

Polyopoly. 2 Stone House, Howey, Llandrindod, Wells, Powys LD1 5PL
Tel: 01597 825517

ROSALINE DESIGNS

Traditionally designed Norwegian buttons and clasps, handmade pewter clasps.

Rosaline Designs. Ardmore Lodge, Edderton, Ross-Shire, Scotland IV19 1LB
Tel: 01862 821246 Fax: 01862 821348

SYLVANNA LLEWELYN

Buttons from ancient to modern, specialising in brass livery buttons, 1920's - 1960's glass buttons, quantities of 30's - 40's plastic buttons, plastics to precious antique buttons.

Sylvanna Llewelyn. Shop 33, The Antique Centre, 151 Sydney Street, Chelsea, London SW3 6NT
Tel: 0171 351 4981 Fax: 0171 565 0003

TALISMAN

Button range.

Talisman. 29 Coutts Avenue, Shorne, Gravesend, Kent DA12 3HJ
Tel: 01474 822960

TERATA LTD

Smart and novelty buttons. Trade and retail via mail order.

Terata Ltd. PO Box 231, Hounslow, Middlesex TW3 2TA
Tel: 020 8395 7138 Fax: 020 8395 6479

VINTAGE L. NICHOLS GLASS BUTTONS

L. Nichols was a lone glass maker who made handmade couture buttons from 1946-1966 in London's Marylebone. His original buttons are for sale through his daughter.

Vintage L. Nichols Glass Buttons. 35 Addington Square, London SE5 7LB
Tel: 020 7701 3433 nicbutns @ lineone.net

VOGUE STAR LTD

Specialists in buttons, buckles and motifs for all occasions.

Vogue Star Ltd. Forum House, Rake Industries, Rogate, Nr Petersfield, Hampshire GU31 5DU
Tel: 01730 894208 Fax: 01730 894221

ASPIRE 2

Computer software for textile design.

Aspire 2. Strathspey, Pentre Hill, Flint Mountain, Flintshire CH6 5Q
Tel: 01352 761798 Fax: 01352 761798

COCHENILLE DESIGN STUDIO

Computer software and design products for stitchers, knitters, beaders and other textile and craft artists. Stitch painter, a grid based paint programme, garment styles for creating non-structured garments. Mail order available.

**Cochenille Design Studio. c/o Gillian Lamb, 16 Firwood Close,
St. John's, Woking, Surrey GI21 1UQ**
Tel: 01483 476356

COMPUTER TEXTILE DESIGN GROUP

Embroidery, patchwork, quilting, surface design, dress, knitting, lace making, screen printing, beading and many other related skills.
Annual membership, access to library of computer textile designs and the textile collection.

**Computer Textile Design Group. Galleybirds, Fielden Road, Crowborough,
East Sussex TN6 1TP**
Tel: 01892 669030

DESIGN INSPIRATIONS LTD

Design Inspirations is the the resource centre for the design professional. We specialise in offering a computer aided design services to fashion, knitwear and textile designers alike.

**Design Inspirations Ltd. Unit 5, Nottingham Fashion Centre, Huntingdon Street,
Nottingham NG1 3LH**
Tel/Fax: 0115 9505698

FOXWOOD DESIGNS LTD
THE ELECTRIC DESIGN LIBRARY

Hundreds of designs for Japanese Electronics

Foxwood Designs Ltd. Stream House, Castle Hill, Rotherfield, East Sussex TN6 3RU

INSYS INTERACTIVE SYSTEMS LTD
PAD SYSTEM TECHNOLOGY

Pad System Software is a designer tool for grading and marking, pattern design, style design, combining tasks usually executed by different people.

Insys Interactive Systems Ltd. 3D Mackenzie Road, London N7 8QZ
Tel: 020 7700 6164 Fax: 020 7700 6687

MACSOLUTIONS

Books and software for textile and knit designs for a range of different computers.

MacSolutions. 24 Cliffe Terrace, Keighley, West Yorkshire BD21 5DP

PAD SYSTEM TECHNOLOGY

Pad System Software is a designer tool for grading and marking, pattern design, style design, combining tasks usually executed by different people.

Insys Interactive Systems Ltd. 3D Mackenzie Road, London N7 8QZ
Tel: 020 7700 6164 Fax: 020 7700 6687

PAINTED LADY PATTERNS ELECTRONIC DESIGNS

SAE for details.

Painted Lady Patterns Electronic Designs. 44 Cumberland Street, Workington, Cumbria CA14 2QP

SOFT BYTE LTD

Fittingly Sew - Computer aided design for pattern drafting, print out full size pattern on desk top printer. Designaknit - computer aided design for creating garment shaping, stitch patterns, print diagrams, machine interfaces.

Soft Byte Ltd. Quarry Lane, Nantmawr, Oswestry, Shropshire SY10 9HH
Tel: 01691 828556 Fax: 01691 828195

TECHNOLOGY FOR TEXTILES

Courses for teachers and students.

Technology for Textiles. 'Galleybirds', Fielden Road, Crowborough TN6 1TP
Tel: 01892 669030

URSA SOFTWARE

Computer software for cross stitch and tapestry design.

Ursa Software. 17 Camborne Grove, Gateshead, Tyne & Wear NE8 4EX
Tel/Fax: 0191 4775293

WEAVERY

Weave design software for Mac and PC. Demo disks available. Individual or group training and "Hands-on-Workshop" for Guilds and other groups.

Weavery. 24 Cliffe Terrace, Keighley, West Yorkshire BD21 5DPP
Tel: 01535 691077 Fax: 01535 691078

Remember to mention the
FASHION & TEXTILE
INFORMATION DIRECTORY
When ordering your supplies

FATEC
FASHION
AND
TEXTILE
EDUCATIONAL
CONSULTANCY

AMBERLEY CRAFTS

Tatting and crochet cottons.

Amberley Crafts. 31 Huddlestone Road, Forest Gate, London E7 0AN

ANNA'S LACE CHEST

Crochet, bobbin lace, needle lace, lace knitting and tape lace. Mail order service. Catalogue available on request.

Anna's Lace Chest. 1 Gorse Close, Whitehills, Northampton NN2 8ED
Tel: 01604 461536

ASHILL DYED YARNS

Walnut crochet hooks and knitting needles.

Ashill Dyed Yarns. Pindon End Cottage, Pindon End, Hanslope, Milton Keynes MK19 7HN
Tel: 01908 510277

CROCHET DESIGN

Comprehensive mail order supplier for all crochet needs including: library of videos, books, patterns, accessories, tools (broomstick, Tunisian, hairpin, handled and traditional hooks), plus vocational Distance Learning Diploma. SAE for catalogue and price list.

Crochet Design. 17 Poulton Square, Morecambe LA4 5PZ
Tel: 01524 831752 Fax: 01524 833099

CROCHET TOO U.K

Crochet equipment, yarns and supplies.

Crochet Too UK. 248 Shawfield Road, Ash, Nr Aldershot, Hampshire GU12 5DJ
Tel: 01252 334855 Fax: 01252 314558

HOLLYOAK CROCHET

Mail order suppliers for all crochet needs: crochet/Tunisian hooks, broomsticks, hairpins prongs, large selection of books and leaflets, cottons, yarns and accessories. .

Hollyoak Crochet. Cogshall Lane, Comberbach, Cheshire CW9 6BS
Tel: 01606 891660

THE KNITTING & CROCHET GUILD

The leading national organisation for the promotion of knitting and crochet: The practice, preservation, development and continuance of skills. Mail order available for all resources. Guild Journal - Slipknot, gives advice and guidance on relevant topic areas.

The Knitting & Crochet Guild. 228 Chester Road North, Kidderminster, Worcestershire DY10 1TH
Tel: 01562 754367

TATTING & DESIGN

Over 70 coloured crochet and tatting threads. 20gr, 50gr and 100gr balls, Turkish cottons ideal for crochet, tatting (shuttle lace), tatting equipment and books available by mail order.

Tatting & Design. 47 Breedon Hill Road, Derby DE23 6TH
Tel/Fax: 01332 383841

TWILLEYS OF STAMFORD

Crochet yarns and stranded cottons. Mail order and exhibitions only.

Twilleys of Stamford. Roman Mill, Stamford, Lincolnshire PE9 1BG
Tel: 01780 752661 Fax: 01780 765215

WOOL N' THINGS & CROCHET TOO

Stockists of English and American patterns, books, threads, embroidery, crochet hooks, haberdashery and accessories.

Wool N' Things & Crochet Too. 248 Shawfield Road, Ash,
Nr Aldershot, Hampshire GU12 5DJ
Tel/Fax: 01252 334855

ART EXPRESS

Everything you need to get started in silk printing, guides to printing, AV Gutta resist, Thai tissue paper, AV "Iron Fix" Silk colours, silk fabrics etc.

Art Express. Index House, 70 Burley Road, Leeds LS3 1JX
Tel: 0800 731 4185 Fax: 0113 243 6074

ASHILL COLOUR STUDIO

Specialist supplier of natural plant dyes, mordants and books on dyeing. Mail order only. Send SAE for price list.

Ashill Colour Studio. Jenny Dean, Boundary Cottage, 172 Clifton Road, Shefford, Bedfordshire SG17 5AH
Tel: 01462 812001

CANDLE MAKER SUPPLIERS

Batik dyeing equipment and dyes.

Candle Maker Suppliers. 28 Blythe Road, London W14 0HA
Tel: 020 7602 403112

CRAFT BASICS

Suppliers of needlework, Rowan knitting and craft materials: Silk and fabric paints, feathers, beads, unusual threads etc. Mail order. Telephone enquiries welcome.

Craft Basics. 9 Gillygate, York Y03 7EA
Tel: 01904 652840 Fax: 01904 652 840

THE DYERS HAND

Hand dyed painted cottons, silks, satins and velvets. Procion dyes and fabrics for dyeing. Mail order, trade enquiries and personal callers welcome by appointment.

The Dyers Hand. Sandra Wyman, 1 Welton Road, Leeds LS6 1EE
Tel/Fax: 0113 224 9877

DYLON INTERNATIONAL LTD

Manufacturer of consumer fabric dyes and household products, including fabric dyes and paints.

Dylon International Ltd. Worsley Bridge Road, Lower Sydenham, London SE26 5HD
Tel: 020 8663 4801 Fax: 020 8658 6735

THE FABRIC COLOUR WORKSHOP

Silk painting, paints, dyes and glass painting kits and all supplies, equipment and accessories. ARTY'S silk and cotton ranges, silk, velvet (plain and devoré) scarves by the metre. Lectures, demonstrations and workshops. Mail order.

The Fabric Colour Workshop. 91 Fleetgate, Barton-upon-Humber, North Lincolnshire DN18 5QD
Tel: 01652 636318 Fax: 01652 636318

FASHION N' FOIL MAGIC

Suppliers of foils, adhesives for the textile and printing industries, easy to use, also for use with photocopiers. Instruction video. Mail order catalogue on request.

Fashion n' Foil Magic. PO Box 3746, London N2 9DE
Tel: 020 8444 1992 Fax: 020 8883 0485

FIBRECRAFTS

Spinning, weaving and dyeing supplies, textile books, videos and magazines on the textile arts. Dyestuffs and chemicals for dyeing and batik. International mail order.

Fibrecrafts. 1 Old Portsmouth Road, Peasmarsh, Guildford, Surrey GU3 1LZ
Tel: 01483 421853 Fax: 01483 419960

FRAMEWORK ART & CRAFT

Everything for the silk painter: silk dyes, fabrics etc.

Framework Art & Craft. 63 Penbroke Centre, Cheyney Manor Industrial Estate, Swindon, Wiltshire SN2 2PQ
Tel: 01793 51309

GEORGE WEIL & SONS LTD

For silk painters, textile dyers and screen printers. Serious products at sensible prices.

George Weil & Sons Ltd. 1 Old Portsmouth Road, Peasmarsh, Guildford GU3 1LZ
Tel: 01483 421853 Fax: 01483 419960

G.I.L.L.S.E.W.

Indian printing blocks, discharge paste, fibrefilm, xpandaprint, softsculpt etc.
Suppliers' of all those little extras, you cannot do without.

G.I.L.L.S.E.W. Boundary House, Moor Common, Lane End, Buckinghamshire HP14 3HR
Tel: 01494 881886

HELEN RIPPIN (WARATAH FIBRES)

Gaywool dyes from Australia suitable for wool, silk, mohair, also specialises in hand painted and hand dyed fibres. Workshops, demonstrations and mail order.

Helen Rippin (Waratah Fibres). 3 Kirkham Street, Rodley LS13 1JP
Tel: 0113 2557198 Fax: 0113 2557198

KEMTEX COLOURS
KEMTEX SERVICES LTD

Suppliers of small quantities (50gms - 5 Kilos) of textile dyes: Procion, acid, direct, disperse, and Indigo plus a wide range of associated chemicals. Send SAE for details.

Kemtex Services Ltd. Chorley Business and Technology Centre, Euxton Lane, Chorley, Lancashire PR7 6TE
Tel: 01257 230220 Fax: 01257 230225

M & R DYES

Small dye company supplying craft textiles. Reactives, milling acids, natural dyes, mordants, chemicals, yarns including: silks and fibres. Tuition available. Mail order- send SAE for catalogue.

M & R Dyes. Carters, Station Road, Wickham Bishops, Witham, Essex CM8 3JB
Tel: 01621 891405 Fax: 01621 893528

N.E.S ARNOLD

Art, craft and printing materials.

N.E.S Arnold. Ludlow Hill Road, West Bridgford, Nottingham NG2 6HD
Tel: 0115 945 2000

NOEL DYRENFORTH

Procion reactive dye supplier - mail order.

Noel Dyrenforth. 11 Shepherds Hill, London N6 5QJ
Tel/Fax: 0181 348 0956

POTHE HILL & COMPANY

Wax manufacturers.

Pothe Hill & Company. High Street, Stratford, London
Tel: 020 8534 7091

'PURE SILK'

White silk scarves with fine hand rolled edges. Send SAE for sample.

'Pure Silk' The Old Church Room, Hill Row, Haddenham, Cambridgeshire CB6 3TL

OMEGA DYES

A comprehensive range of dyes and acid dyes. Procion, direct dyes, for cotton
and other cellulose fibres, plus acid dyes for wool. Please send SAE for details.

Omega Dyes. 10 Corsend Road, Hartpury, Gloucester GL19 3BP
Tel: 01452 700492

QUALITY COLOURS (LONDON) LTD

Suppliers' of film, fashion, art/design, educational dyestuffs, binders, screens, auxillaries, etc.
Mail order available.

Quality Colours (London) Ltd. Unit 13, Gemini Project, Landmann Way, London SE14 5RL
Tel: 020 7394 8775 Fax: 020 7237 1044

RAINBOW SILKS

Silk painting and fabric decoration supplies and kits. ARTY'S silks, silk viscose velvets, fibre-etch
for devoré, image transfer paper, paints, dyes, frames etc. Mail order service available.

Rainbow Silks. 27 New Road, Amersham, Buckinghamshire HP6 6LD
Tel: 01494 727003 Fax: 01494 724101

SPECIALIST CRAFTS LTD

Mail order supplier of print and craft materials: fabrics, screen printing equipment and
materials, over 9000 items available in total.

Specialist Crafts Ltd. PO Box 247, Leicester LE1 9QS
Tel: 0116 251 0405 Fax: 0116 251 0105

SUASION LTD

Distributors of Jacquard textile paints and dyes. Printing equipment, steamers, frames,
Toray brushes, specialist silks and velvets to devorés. London showroom for Sinotex UK -
The ARTY'S catalogue.

Suasion Ltd. 35 Riding House Street, London W1P 7PT
Tel: 020 7580 3763 Fax: 020 7636 4287

TEXTILE EXPRESSION

Embroidery and textile products by mail order, including handmade papers, dyes, paints and printing materials. Mail order catalogue available.

Textile Expression. 31 Belmount Road, Burton upon Trent, Staffordshire
DE13 9NL Tel: 01283 520496 Fax: 01283 520878

TEXTILE TECHNIQUES

Textiles and tools direct from Indonesia. Batik equipment : cantings, tjantings, caps, waxes, cottons from Java, dyes - procion cold water, wax pots, traditional Indonesian fabrics. Ikat and batik making equipment. Mail order service and workshops.

Textile Techniques. 37 High Street, Bishop's Castle, Shropshire SY9 5BE
Tel: 01588 638712

VYCOMBE ARTS

Fabric and silk paints, paints, dyes (including Procion), transfer paints, guttas, glass paints, equipment for marbling, accessories. 2 x 1st class stamps for catalogue.

Vycombe Arts. Fen Way, Fen Walk, Woodbridge, Suffolk IP12 4AS
Tel/Fax: 01394 380882

WARATAH FIBRES

Gaywool dyes from Australia suitable for wool, silk, mohair, also specialises in hand painted and hand dyed fibres. Workshops, demonstrations and mail order.

Helen Rippin (Waratah Fibres). 3 Kirkham Street, Rodley LS13 1JP
Tel: 0113 2557198 Fax: 0113 2557198

Waratah Fibres

Importing Dyes & Fibres from Australia

European Distributor for

GAYWOOL

Colours of Australia

- **32 Vibrant Dye shades for Wool, Silk, Mohair and Angora**

- **Unique blends of fibres also available**

- **Versitile all in one Acid Dyes suitable for Shibori, Silk Paper as well as Yarn and Fleece Dyeing**

- **Gaywool Slivers of Merino/Silk and Merino/Mohair suitable for Spinners and Felters**

For further information please send an S.A.E to:-
Helen Rippin, 3 Kirkham Street, Rodley, Leeds LS13 1JP.
Tel/Fax: 0113 2557198

Shade cards available on request for dyes, Merino/Mohair or Merino/Silk £2 per card

JANICE WILLIAMS

Goldwork and Japanese embroidery specialist. Metal threads, beads, silks and a wide range of textile books. Mail order, send 2 x 1st class stamps for price list.

Janice Williams. Sheldon Cottage Studio, Epney, Saul, Gloucester GL2 7LN
Tel: 01452 740639

JAPANESE EMBROIDERY CENTRE UK

Finest Japanese reeled filament silk in a wide range of colours, metallic threads, Japanese embroidery designs, tools and accessories for traditional Japanese embroidery and other textile arts. Tuition, courses available. Mail order.

Japanese Embroidery Centre UK. C/o White Lodge, Littlewick Road, Lower Knaphill, Surrey GU21 2JU
Tel: 01483 476246 Fax: 01483 836152

KALEN CRAFTS

Cross stitch specialists, also stocking embroidery threads, kits and accessories. Mail order.

Kalen Crafts. 5 Springfield Centre, Orchard Street, Kempston, Bedfordshire MK42 7PR
Tel: 01234 843323 Fax: 01234 855966

K C Craft

Retail outlet with mail order. Haberdashery, tapestry, beadcraft, stamps, ribbon, embroidery and bobbin lace. DMC Agent, cross stitch supplies plus full range of Pergamano and Pinflair.

K C Craft. 11 High Street, Sandy, Bedfordshire SG19 1AS
Tel: 01767 691190 Fax: 01767 680042

LADY PENELOPE'S NEEDLECRAFTS

One of the largest and finest selections of needlework threads, fabrics, accessories and absoloutely everything for the needleworker. Mail order worldwide. Price list available.

Lady Penelope's Needlecrafts. 8 Station Road, Parkstone, Poole, Dorset BH14 8UB
Tel/Fax: 01202 735881

L & B EMBROIDERY

Small fabric packs and teaching material packs, spaced dyed threads.
Mail order, embroidery workshops.

L & B Embroidery. 28 Leigh Road, Andover, Hampshire SP10 2AP
Tel/Fax: 01264 365102

LEANDA

Specialist manufacturers of traditional equipment for Japanese braiding and tassel making. Also makers of items for embroidery, spinning and weaving. Mail order, trade and retail. Courses available.

Leanda. Scotts Yard, Ber Street, Norwich NR1 3HA
Tel: 01603 763340 Fax: 01603 765314

LOWERY WORKSTANDS

Manufacturers, retailers and wholesalers of steel embroidery workstands and accessories. Stretcher frames, blocking frames, illuminated magnifyers for fine work suitable for embroidery, lace work, cross stitch, reading etc. Mail order available.

Lowery Workstands. Bentley Lane, Grasby, Barnetby, North Lincolnshire DN38 6AW
Tel/Fax: 01652 628240

MACHINE MART LTD

Magnifying Lamp ideal for close-up work, model makers, jewellers, embroidery etc.

Machine Mart Ltd. 211 Lower Parliament Street. Nottingham NG1 1GN
Tel: 0115 9561811 Fax: 0115 9562900

MAC CULLOCH & WALLIS LTD

Mail order, wholesale and retail. Specialist embroidery threads, haberdashery, trimmings, fabrics, millinery supplies, linings and interlinings, silk, bridal fabrics, trimmings and tailoring.

Mac Culloch & Wallis Ltd. 25-26 Dering Street, London W1R OBH
Tel: 020 7629 0311 Fax: 020 7491 9578

MADEIRA THREADS (UK) LTD

Manufacturers of high quality machine embroidery, sewing and decorative threads. Non-woven backings, needles and all embroidery ancilliaries for industry and retail use. International mail order company, manufacturer and distributors..

Madeira Threads (UK) Ltd. PO Box 6, Thirsk, North Yorkshire YO7 3YZ
Tel: 01845 524880 Fax: 01845 525046

MADRA DUBH FABRICS & THREADS LTD

Fabrics, beads and threads.

Madra Dubh Fabrics & Threads Ltd. Gan Crioch, Rathcooney, Glanmire, Cork, Ireland
Tel/Fax: 0035321 821206

THE MULBERRY DYER

Handspun naturally dyed embroidery silks. Mail order.

The Mulberry Dyer. Maes Gwyn, Rhewl, Ruthin, Denbighshire LL15 1UL
Tel: 01824 703616

MULBERRY SILKS

Hand wound packs of embroidery silks in beautiful colour schemes for embroiderers and lace-makers.

Mulberry Silks. Patricia Wood, 2 Old Rectory Cottages, Easton Grey, Malmesbury, Wiltshire SN16 0PE
Tel: 01666 840881

NEEDLECRAFT

Embroidery threads, tapestry threads, canvas, kits, silks, wools, needles, books, frames etc. Mail order service available. All major credit cards accepted.

Needlecraft. 1797 Coventry Road, Yardley, Birmingham B26 1DS
Tel: 0121 742 1141

NEEDLECRAFT CENTRE - LONGLEAT

Located in the stables alongside Longleat House is the needlecraft centre selling a wide range of speciilst products. Plus courses, exhibitions and specialist embroidery tours of Longleat House.

Needlecraft Centre - Longleat. Stable Courtyard, Longleat, Warminster, Wiltshire BA12 7NL
Tel: 01985 844774 Fax: 01985 844907

OLIVER TWISTS

Hand dyed threads, fabrics and fibres for both traditional and creative embroiderers. Experimental packs for the textile enthusiast.

Oliver Twists. Jean Oliver, 34 Holmands Park, Chester le Street, Co. Durham DH3 3PJ
Tel/Fax: 0191 388 8233

PERIVALE-GUTERMANN LTD

Manufacturers and distributors of sewing threads to the industrial and home sewing markets. Distributors of YKK retail zips. Suppliers' of the new range of Gütermann 'Creativ'. Embroidery threads, materials and equipment.

Perivale-Gutermann Ltd. Wadsworth Road, Greenford, Middlesex UB6 7JS
Tel: 020 8998 5000 Fax: 020 8991 1344

PICK N' CHOOSE

Range of sewing, cross stitch and craft materials. DMC main agents, Coats, Anchor, needlework specialists. Framecraft stockists. Free mail order catalogue.

Pick N' Choose. 56 Station Road, Northwich, Cheshire CW9 5RB
Tel: 01606 41523 Fax: 01606 47255

P J THREADS

Embroidery threads.

P J Threads. 114 Kiln Lane, Eccleston, St. Helens, Merseyside WA10 4RJ
Tel: 01744 731702

PROSPECTS (MAIL ORDER)

Silk, fabric and thread packs.

Prospects (Mail Oder). Prospect House, Smithy Lane, Preesall, Poulton-le-Fylde, Lancashire FY6 0NJ
Tel: 01253 811523

PUNCH PEOPLE LTD.

Punchloop Embroidery starter kits and accessories.

Punch People. PO Box 69, Egham, Surrey TW20 0NY
Tel/Fax: 01784 439318

READICUT WOOL

Threads, kits, charts, fabric and accessories.

Readicut Wool. Terry Mills, Westfield Road, Horbury, Wakefield, West Yorkshire WF4 6HD
Tel: 01924 810811 Fax: 01924 810813

R & R ENTERPRISES

Lap frames.

R & R Enterprises. 13 Frederick Road, Malvern, Worcestershire WR14 1RS
Tel: 01684 563235

SEW & SO'S

Specialising in embroidery, patchwork and quilting supplies. Also offering workshops and courses. Mail order service.

Sew & So's. 16 Upper Olland Street, Bungay, Suffolk NR35 1BG
Tel: 01986 896147 Fax: 01986 896147

SEW-IT-ALL-LTD.

Cross stitch and embroidery fabrics, threads and braids

Sew-It-All-Ltd. The Warehouse, 24 Chandof Road, Buckinghamshire MK18 1AL
Tel: 0800 7314563 Fax: 01280 814818

SHELDON COTTAGE STUDIOS

Gold work and Japanese embroidery specialist. Metal threads, beads, silks and a wide range of textile books. Mail order. 2 x 1st class stamps for price list.

Sheldon Cottage Studios. Epney, Saul, Gloucester GL2 7LN
Tel: 01452 740639

SIESTA FRAMES

Interlocking bar frames, plastic clip frames, Able stretcher frames, Posilock floor stands, Sonata seat frames, clip on magnifyers etc.

Siesta Frames. PO Box 1759, Ringwood, Hampshire BH24 3XN
Tel/Fax: 01202 813363

SILKEN STRANDS

Mail order suppliers of machine and hand embroidery threads in industrial and domestic sizes: rayons, cottons, silks and metalics. Imported Indian plain and variegated rayons. Dissolving fabrics including Aquafilm. Gimp for tassels and a range of leathers, real slusha etc.

Silken Strands. 20 Y Rhos, Bangor, Gwynedd LL57 2LT
Tel/Fax: 01248 362361

SMUGGLERS NEEDLECRAFT CENTRE

10,000 different threads: Anchor, Rainbow Gallery, Madeira, 1000+ fabrics.
Retail and mail order around the world.

Smugglers Needlecraft Centre. 3 Capstone Place, Ilfracombe, North Devon EX34 9TQ
Tel/Fax: 01271 863457

STABLECRAFT

Mail order - split box quantities. Anchor stranded cotton and tapisserie wools, Sylko and Drima sewing threads, hand and machine sewing needles. All available in singles.

Stablecraft. Unit 8, Hardwicke Stables, Hadnell, Shrewsbury SY4 4AR
Tel/Fax: 01939 210790

STEF FRANCIS

Space dyed threads and fabrics. Exciting range of hand-dyed silk and cotton threads and fabric in a kaleidoscope of subtly blended colours. Metal, copper, brass and linen threads for hand and machine embroidery. Experimental kits for the textile enthusiast.

Stef Francis. Waverley, Higher Rocombe, Newton Abbot, Devon TQ12 4QL
Tel/Fax: 01803 323004

STICKY STITCHES

Cross stitch charts, canvases and threads.

Sticky Stitches. 17A Junction Road, Burgess Hill, West Sussex
Tel: 01444 247896

THE STITCH COMPANY

Collection of DMC stranded cottons.

The Stitch Company. 9 Norton Drive, Ford, Salisbury SP4 6DA
Tel: 01722 330098

TEAZLE EMBROIDERIES

Crewel and tapestry threads, patterns, Persian yarn, textured yarns, beads and sequins, canvases, books, embroidery accessories and lots more.

Teazle Embroideries. Suzanne Flew and Eileen Chapman, 35 Boothferry Road, Hull HU3 6UA
Tel: 01482 572531

TEXERE YARNS

Wool, silk, glitter, mohair, cotton, acrylic and ribbon yarns for embroidery and other textile crafts. Mail order or visit the mill. Personal visitors welcome.

Texere Yarns. College Mill, Barkerend Road, Bradford BD3 9AQ
Tel: 01274 722191 Fax: 01274 393500

TEXTILE ART PROJECTS

Creative stitching kits using hand dyed fabrics and threads for patchwork, quilting, embroidery and the textile arts. Shimmering silks, glittering threads, quilting and embroidery templates, fabric bases, space dyed silks and much more.

Textile Art Projects. 4 Mount Pleasant, Harbertonford, Totnes Devon TQ9 7TG
Tel: 01803 732167 E-mail: natasha @ realitycom.com

TEXTILE EXPRESSION

Fabrics for modern and traditional embroidery, textures in variety from hessian to cotton velvet, dyes and colour media, decorative and metallic threads. Mail order.

Textile Expression. 31 Belmot Road, Tutbury, Burton on Trent, Staffordshire DE13 9NL
Tel: 01283 520496 Fax: 01283 520878

TEXTILE HARVEST

Exciting and unusual fabrics in small quantities and small sized pieces for embroiderers and craftworkers. Silks, organzas, metallics, velvets, leathers, metal foil, handmade papers and barkcloth. Also some basic fabrics available. Mail order.

Textile Harvest. 20 Old Malt Way, Horsell, Woking, Surrey GU21 4QD
Tel: 01483 764941

THORNTON NEEDLECRAFTS

Embroidery threads, charts, presentation cards, cross stitch supplies, linens and beads etc. Mail order only.

Thornton Needlecrafts. Thornton Park Farm, Bunkers Hill, New York, Lincoln LN4 4YL
Tel/Fax: 01205 280781

THREADNEEDLE HOUSE

Fabrics, threads, canvases, kits, charts, and fabrics.

Threadneedle House. 9 Nuneham Courtenay, Oxford OX44 9NX
Tel: 01865 343407

THREADS N' THINGS

For the creative embroiderer. Hand and machine threads: silk, rayon, metallic, and space-dyed. Japanese beads, organzas and other fabrics.

Threads n' Things. 23 Fronks Avenue, Harwich, Essex C012 3RX
Tel: 012555 504776

TWENTY-FIRST CENTURY YARNS

Hand-dyed threads, fine silks, silk boucle, silk & wool, wool slub gimp, mixed textured bags, cotton chenille, tubular cotton tape etc.

Twenty-First Century Yarns. Unit 15, Earl Soham Lodge, Earl Soham, Suffolk IP13 7SA
Tel: 01394 387659

UNICRAFT DESIGN

Lap top embroidery frames.

Unicraft Design. 41 Welbeck Avenue, Hinckley, Leicestershire L10 2JH
Tel: 01455 635376

VARIEGATIONS

Mail order only, supplier of unusual fabrics, embroidery fabrics, colour theme packs, papers, metals, hand dyed threads, books, accessories including transfer foils, 'Heat It' craft tool, fibres, metal meshes, discharge, dissolvables, devoré and more.

Variegations. Rose Cottage, Harper Royd Lane, Norland, Halifax HX6 3QQ
Tel: 01422 832411

VICTORIA FLOYD - HAND DYED TEXTILES

A unique collection of hand dyed threads and yarns. Hand dyed worked papers.
Please contact for sales tables and mail order details. Yarns: viscose, cotton, rayon, cotton slubs, cotton & acrylics, linen, chenille, space and flat dyed yarns.

Victoria Floyd - Hand Dyed Textiles. 5 Field End, Stourport-on-Severn, Worcestershire PY13 8UD
Tel: 01299 823875

THE VOIRREY EMBROIDERY CENTRE

The Voirrey Embroidery Centre - Embroidery materials, kits and accessories, tapestry, patchwork and quilting. Exhibitions and courses. Mail order. Open 7 days a week.

The Voirrey Embroidery Centre. Brimstage Hall, Wirral CH63 6JA
Tel: 0151 342 3514 Fax: 0151 342 5161

VYCOMBE ARTS

Silk fabrics, paints, dyes, silk embroidery threads, fabrics, foils, glitter dust, embroidery puff paints, dissolvable fabrics, plus much more.

Vycombe Arts. Fen Way, Fen Walk, Woodbridge, Suffolk IP12 4AS
Tel/Fax: 01394 380882

WESTEND LACE AND EMBROIDERY SUPPLIES

Threads, charts and kits.

Westend Lace and Embroidery Supplies. Yvonne Close, Orchid Cottage, Drury Lane, Mortimer Common, Reading RG7 2JN
Tel: 01189 332670 Fax: 01189 331490

WILLOW FABRICS

Over 620 fabrics and canvases in stock: cottons, linens, hardanger, tapestry and rug canvases, also stock embroidery threads, yarns and kits.

Willow Fabrics. 95 Town Lane, Mobberley, Knutsford, Cheshire WA16 7HH
Tel: 01565 872225 Fax: 01565 872239

WORLD EMBROIDERY SUPPLIES

Beads, bells, shells, shisha, hand dyed threads, fabrics and other specialist supplies.
Costume and textiles from Asia. Talks, workshops and mail order service available.

World Embroidery Supplies. 2 Woodlands, Kirby Misperton, Malton, North Yorkshire Y017 6XW
Tel: 01653 668419

WYE NEEDLECRAFT

2000 charts/booklets, 250 fabrics/canvases, 70 types of threads/wools. Postal service available.
Wye Needlecraft open 6½ days a week.

Wye Needlecraft. Clive and Rosemary Sheridan, 2 Royal Oak Place, Matlock Street, Bakewell, Derbyshire DE45 1HD
Tel: 01629 815198 Fax: 01629 814100

BRITISH KNITTING & CLOTHING EXPORT COUNCIL

Trade association promoting exports from the UK of all apparel and fashion accessories. Associate members include suppliers to the clothing trade.

British Knitting & Clothing Exports Council. 5 Portland Place, London W1N 3AA
Tel: 020 7636 788 Fax: 020 7636 7515

BRITISH MENSWEAR GUILD

The British Menswear Guild Ltd is a an export sales and marketing led trade association of high quality branded menswear. The guild activities are focused on export promotion, representing Britain's finest branded mens clothing and accessory manufacturers.

British Menswear Guild Ltd. 1 Saville Row, London W1X 2JR
Tel: 020 7734 6211 Fax: 020 7734 6277

CREATIVE EXHIBITIONS LTD

Organisers of the Knitting and Stitching Show.

Creative Exhibitions Ltd. 34 Lewisham Park, London SE13 6Q2
Tel: 020 8690 8888

CREATIVE INDUSTRIES ASSOCIATIONS

Promotes and gives the industry a higher profile, offering help and advice to both new and established businesses.

Creative Industries Associations. PO Box 2238, Christchurch BH23 5YR
Tel: 01425 272711 Fax: 01425 279369

DALESWAY FESTIVALS LTD

Festival of craft, fashion and design.

Dalesway festivals Ltd. The All England Jumping Course, London Road, Hickstead, West Sussex RH17 5NX
Tel: 01273 833884 Fax: 01273 835556

GROSVENOR EXHIBITIONS LTD
EXHIBITIONS ORGANISERS

Grosvenor House, London Road, Spalding, Lincolnshire PE11 2TN
Tel: 01775 722900 or 01775 712100

ICHF LTD

Exhibition organisers for the following shows: Creative Stitches and Crafts Alive, ICHF Stitches, Hobbycrafts etc.

ICHF Ltd. Dominic House, Seaton Road, Highcliffe, Dorset BH23 5HW
Tel: 01425 272711 Fax: 01425 279369

CLOTH OF GOLD
Retail dress fabric shop with mail order service. Latest fashion fabrics and specialists in evening and bridal wear fabrics.

Cloth of Gold. 126 High Street, Wootten Bassett, Swindon, Wiltshire SN4 7AU
Tel: 01793 853908

THE CLOTH SHOP
Retail outlet: silks, felts, fake furs, calico and many unusual fabrics.

The Cloth Shop. 290 Portobello Road, London W10 5TE
Tel: 020 8968 6001

COPELAND LINENS LTD
PO Box 95, 59 Bromley Street, Belfast BT13 2EX
Tel: 01232 321065

COZENS FABRICS
Silks, suitings, leisure and fur fabrics, braids, trimmings, vilenes, zips (open ended and invisible), patterns and large haberdashery department.

Cozens Fabrics. 9-11 High Street, Alton, Hampshire GU34 1AW
Tel: 01420 84386 Fax: 01420 80858

CRAFTSWOMAN FABRICS
Mail order service and also factory showroom. Evening and exotic fabrics, linen, linen looks and linen-blends, budget price collections, bride and bridesmaid fabric collections and trimmings. Specialists in bridal and bridesmaid wear and trimmings. Large haberdashery department. Catalogue available.

Craftswoman Fabrics. 1st Floor, Unit 1, Kilroot Business Park, Carrickfergus BT38 7PR
Tel: 01960 351277 Fax: 01960 357630

CRESCENT TRADING
Traders and sellers of all types of clothing fabrics at clearance prices.
Always large stock available.

Crescent Trading. Unit 7, Silwex House, Quaker Street, London E1 6SN
Tel: 020 7377 5067 Fax: 020 7377 5073

CROFT MILL - J. W. COATES
Fabrics and haberdashery: Sheetings, curtainings, dress fabrics, leisure cloths, silks, lycras available by direct mail order.

Croft Mill - J. W. Coates. Lowther Lane, Foulridge, Colne, Lancashire BB12 9QA
Tel: 01282 869625 Fax: 01282 870038

CROTTY & CAMPBELL LTD
Brilliant velvet corduroy and simulated fabrics.

Crotty & Campbell Ltd. 63 Margaret Street, London W1N 7FJ
Tel: 020 7580 0332 Fax: 020 7323 5332

C. I. DAVIS & COMPANY LTD (SILK)

Silk fabrics.

C. I. Davis & Company Ltd. 94-96 Seymour Place, London W1
Tel: 020 8723 0895 Fax: 020 8723 7735

DENHOLME VELVETS LTD

Manufacturers of a wide range of velvets for garments in a variety of widths, compositions and finishes including plain, irradescent, embossed, pleated, printed and crushed. Minimum 3 metres. Mail order service available.

Denholme Velvets Ltd. Halifax Road, Denholme, Bradford, West Yorkshire BD13 4EZ
Tel: 01274 832185 Fax: 01274 832646

DERBY HOUSE FABRICS

Suppliers of fashion fabrics to fabric retail stores, manufacturing outlets, mail order and corporate trade. Fabrics suitable for daywear, eveningwear and bridalwear available.

Derby House Fabrics. Derby House, 59 Derby Street, Manchester M8 8HW
Tel: 0161 832 5222 Fax: 0161 832 4839

DESIGNER FABRIC WAREHOUSE

Designer fabrics, dress, bridal fabrics, upholstery and over 8000 soft furnishing fabrics, accessories, haberdashery and trimmings.

Designer Fabric Warehouse. 91-93 Westgate, Grantham, Lincolnshire NG1 6PG
Tel: 01476 570022 Fax: 01476 579333

B. S. DOLLAMORE LTD

White, ivory and coloured hand woven Indian dupion - available in piece lengths and cut lengths. Also large stocks of dyed 100% double silk crêpe, faille, double silk georgette, fuji, chiffon and organza.

B. S. Dollamore Ltd. Burton Road, Castle Gresley, Swadlincote, Derbyshire DE11 9HA
Tel: 01283 217905 Fax: 01283 550119

DONACO DISCOUNT DESIGNER FABRICS

Impressive range of silks, cottons, wools, lace and designer fabrics, designer trims and accessories available. Mail order service available.

Donaco Discount Designer Fabrics. 93 Edgware Road, London W2 2HX
Tel: 020 7262 9700 Fax: 020 7262 6050

A. DUNNICLIFFE

Quality leathers: mixed colours, large pieces available.

A. Dunnicliffe. Tree Tops, Calke Road, Melbourne, Derby DE73 1DL

DYEING TO PLEASE

A range of hand dyed fabrics - stock or dyed to order and fabrics dyed to order. Design consultation. Any size or any amount. Fast friendly service.

Dyeing to Please. 377 Soundwell Road, Kingswood, Bristol BS15 1JN
Tel: 0402 891176

EBOR FABRICS LTD

Fashion fabrics. Exclusively American fabrics, printed cottons, viscose dress fabrics, craft fabrics. Wholesalers, mills open to trade.

Ebor Fabrics Ltd. Embsay Mills, Embsay, Skipton, North Yorkshire BD23 6QF
Tel: 01756 793908 Fax: 01756 700134

EPRA FABRICS LTD

Large range of dress and curtain fabrics, plain and printed polycottons, gingham, bridal fabrics, fur fabrics, glitter and show fabrics. Catalogue: Over 300 swatches of fabrics. Mail order service available or visit. Dress fabrics, velvets and linings.

Epra Fabrics Ltd. 52-56 Brick Lane, London E7 6RV
Tel: 0207 247 1248 Fax: 0207 247 8518

EURO JAPAN LINKS LTD

Shiko fabrics, Japanese cottons and old silk kimono pieces. Flat silk and metalic threads, pure silk cloths all directly imported from Japan. Mail order only.

Euro Japan Links Ltd. 32 Nant Road, Childs Hill, London NW2 2AT
Tel/Fax: 020 8201 9324

EVER TRADING

Wholesaler: imitation fake furs, leopard, lynx, polar bear etc.

Ever Trading. 12 Martindale, East Sheen, London SW14 7AL
Tel: 020 8878 4050 Fax: 020 8876 5717

THE FABRIC COMPANY

Dress, bridal fabrics, silks and curtain fabrics. Retailers and mail order service.

The Fabric Company. 10 Sussex Street, Cambridge CB1 1PA
Tel: 01223 461449 Fax: 01223 366816

FABRIC LAND

Many dress fabrics: crêpe back satins, silk dupion, chiffons, dress nets and haberdashery.
Ring 01202 480802 for full list of Fabric Land outlets.

R. H. FABRICS

Mail order top quality fabrics in wool, silk and cashmere.

R. H. Fabrics. Roblaw Hall, Aikton, Cumbria CA7 0NR
Tel/Fax: 01697 343269

FABRICS DIRECT

Fashion fabrics.

Fabrics Direct. 46 Elfort Road, London N5 1AZ
Tel: 0171 704 2271

FABRICS GALORE

A wide range of fabrics.

Fabrics Galore. 52-54 Lavender Hill, London SW11 5RJ

FABRIC WORLD

Stockists of a wide range of fabrics: dress, bridal, evening and furnishing prints. stockists of designer/ curtain and upholstery fabrics 3000 bolts selling from £4.99-£20 metre. Normally sold at double the price.

Fabric World. 287-289 High Street, Sutton, Surrey SM1 1LL
Tel: 020 8643 5127 Fax: 020 8770 0021

THE FANCY SILK STORE

Large range of silk fabrics.

The Fancy Silk Store. 27 Moat Lane, Birmingham B5 5BD
Tel: 0121 643 7356

THE FANCY SILK STORE

4 floors of fashion, bridal and furnishing fabrics.

The Fancy Silk Store. 122-123 Edgbaston Street, Bullring Centre, Birmingham B5 4QR
Tel/Fax: 0121 643 7356 Fax: 0121 643 8846

FANTASY FABRICS

Retail supplier of an extensive range of fabrics and threads to meet the creative needs of embroiderers and textile artists. Specialists in exotic fabrics and threads: silks, shot and plain organza, metallic nets, plain polyester silks. Glittery, hairy, textured, dyed and other unusual threads. Dissolvable fabrics, catalogue and samples available.

Fantasy Fabrics. Duich Lodge, Croyard Road, Beauly, Inverness, Scotland IV4 7DJ
Tel/Fax: 01463 783606

FANTASY FELT

Handmade felt in silk and merino wool produced in small or large pieces suitable for embroiderers, quilters and textile artists. Special requests can be made up. Mail order. SAE for samples.

Fantasy Felt. 1 St Andrews Road, Lhanbryde, Elgin, Morayshire, Scotland IV30 8NZ
Tel: 01727 865038

THE FENT SHOP

A wide range of fabrics.

The Fent Shop. Pickford Street Mill, Pickford Street, Macclesfield SK11 6HY

FIRED EARTH

Extensive range of fabrics and Shaker cottons. Mail order service. Catalogue available.

Fired Earth. Twyford Mill, Oxford Road, Adderbury, Oxon OX17 3HP
Tel: 01295 812088 Fax: 01295 810832

FLAX MILL

Dress, bridal fabrics and trims. Haberdashery and curtain fabrics.

Flax Mill. Bretherton Row, Wallgate, Wigan, Greater Manchester WN1 1LL
Tel: 01942 242102

FLETCHERS FABRICS LTD

A wide range of fabrics.

Fletchers Fabrics. 8 Odsal House, Font Street, Acomb, York Y024 3BL
Tel: 01904 793885

FOUR D RUBBER COMPANY LTD

Manufacturer of latex sheeting for fashion and fetish clothing. Silk screen printed designs available on request.

Delves Road, Heanor Gate Industrial Estate, Heanor, Derbyshire DE75 7SJ
Tel: 01773 763134 Fax: 01773 763136

FRANK P. KIRK

All over laces, metallic laces, nylon net and tulle, plain and printed stretch fabrics, embroidered and Gui pure laces, velours etc.

Frank P. Kirk. 122 Queens Road East, Beeston, Nottingham NG9 2FD
Tel: 0115 967 7330 Fax: 0115 9677 5303

GALLIA TEXTILES

Importers of a wide range of bridal and eveningwear fabrics from all over the world. Duchesse satin, embroidered silks, brocades, dupion silks, satins in 45 shades, satin back, Shantung /crêpe velvets, lamé, linings, nets, plus much more.

Gallia Textiles. 3-5 Old Montague Street, London E1 5NL
Tel: 020 7377 1705 Fax: 020 7377 2938

GARDINER OF SELKIRK LTD

Tweed Mills, Dunsdale Road, Selkirk, Scotland TD7 5NA
Tel: 01750 20283 Fax: 01750 22525

GAYLIAN FABRICS

American cotton fabrics, picture panels, quilting accessories and kits. Mail order available.

**Gaylian Fabrics. Milton Ernest Garden Centre, Radwell Road,
Milton Ernest, Bedford MK44 1SH**
Tel: 01234 824983

GERRIATS GB

Fabrics for the stage.

Gerriats GB. J412 Tower Bridge Business Complex, Drummond Road, London SE16 4EF

GRAHAM SMITH FABRICS LTD

Fabrics in wool.

**Graham Smith Fabrics Ltd. Goulbourne House, South Street, Keighley,
West Yorkshire BD21 1DD**
Tel: 01535 664162 Fax: 01535 610745

GUL INTERNATIONAL LTD

Suppliers and converters of Neoprene materials.

Gul International Ltd. Callywith Gate Industrial Estate, Bodmin, Cornwall PL31 2RQ
Tel: 01208 72382 Fax: 01208 75218

HARTLEYS MAIL ORDER LTD

Mail order suppliers of fabrics: dress, cottons, poly-cottons, silks, velvet, calico, sheeting, craft, soft furnishings, plus much more. Buyers of redundant stock and clearance fabrics from mill makers etc. Catalogue and samples available.

Hartleys Mail Order Ltd. Regent House, Whitewalls Industrial Estate, Colne, Lancashire BB8 8LJ
Tel: 01282 861350 Fax: 01282 870679

HANSSON OF GUILFORD

Importers and distributors of silks, silk embroideries, wedding silks, French lace. Extensive range of silk dupion, raw silk, cr„µpes, satins, chiffons, organzes, brocades, jacquards, I-Kat checks, stripes, tartans, velvets etc. Show room. Mail order services.

Hansson of Guilford. 108 Woodbridge Road, Guilford, Surrey GU1 4PY
Tel: 01483 451625 Fax: 01483 451602

HANSON'S (DISCOUNT) FABRICS

Cash and carry. All you need to sew. An aladin's cave of fabrics, from calico to silk, enormous ranges, sewing machines, haberdashery, threads, interlinings, dressmaking patterns. The Dressmakers Warehouse.

Hanson's (Discount) Fabrics. Old Station Yard, Station Road, Sturminster, Newton, Dorset DT10 1BD
Tel: 01258 472698 Fax: 01258 473813

HARRINGTON BRIDAL FABRICS & LACES

Bridal fabrics and laces from low cost synthetics to exclusive silks. Mail order catalogue and shade cards available. Show room at Long Eaton.

Harrington Bridal Fabrics & Laces. Turret E, Harrington Mills, Leopald Street, Long Eaton, Nottingham NG10 4QE
Tel: 0115 946 0766 Fax: 0115 946 0741

HENRY BERTRAND

Chinese, Thai and Indian silks. Varying weights, weave, print and handle. Silks also from England, France and other countries.

Henry Bertrand. 11-13 Melton Street, London NW1 2EA
Tel: 020 7383 3868 Fax: 020 7383 4797

HORLEY FABRICS

Leotard lycras - velvet lycras ranges of 20 colours. Mail order only.

Horley Fabrics. 6 Hildas Close, Horley, Surrey RH6 7BA
Tel: 01293 776440

THE HUMPHRIES WEAVING COMPANY LTD

Handloom silk weavers, 20 metre minimum lengths made to order. Silk throwsters, commission yarn dyers, embroidery yarn suppliers, working silk museum. The last commerciallly operated hand loom silk weavers in England.

The Humphries Weaving Company. Devere Mill, Queen Street, Castle Hedingham, Halstead, Essex CO9 3HA
Tel: 01787 461193 Fax: 01787 462701

HUNTERS OF BRORA LTD

Apparel fabrics in wool, silks and linens.

Hunters of Brora Ltd. Brora, Sutherland, Scotland KW9 6NA
Tel: 01408 623500 Fax: 01408 623533

THE ISLE MILL

Wool tartans.

The Isle Mill. 12 West Moulin Road, Pitlochry, Scotland PH16 5AF

ISLE OF MULL WEAVERS

Scottish tweeds and fashion tweeds woven in pure new wool. Samples available by request.

Isle of Mull Weavers. Craig Nure, Isle of Mull, Argyll PA65 6AY
Tel/Fax: 01680 812381

H. JACKSON (FABRICS) LTD

Fashion fabrics for all seasons.

H. Jackson (Fabrics) Ltd. Parliament Street, Nottingham NG1 1GP
Tel: 0115 958 2184

JAGGERHILL TEXTILES LTD

African style batik print specialists, plain cloths and damasks. Primarily wholesale, suppliers to the trade and to educational establishments. Mail order on request.

Jaggerhill Textiles Ltd. 2 Fairfield Street, Manchester M1 3GF
Tel: 0161 237 3077 Fax: 0161 237 3066

JAMES BRINDLEY OF HARROGATE

Stock supported range of silk dupion, silk matka, handspray chiffon, georgette, devoré, velvets (with stretch), silk/linens, plain and jacquards. Authentic Chinese braids.

James Brindley of Harrogate. 29-31 James Street, Harrogate HG1 1QY
Tel: 01423 528677 Fax: 01423 568993

JAMES HARE SILKS

Offer an extensive collection of pure silk and a huge stock of silk mix fabrics from both Europe and every major Far Eastern centre of silk production. No minimum quantities means that you can order exactly the amount you require. Trade enquiries only.

James Hare Silks. PO Box 72, Monarch House, Queen Street, Leeds LS1 1LX
Tel: 0113 2431204 Fax: 0113 2433525

JASON'S

Couture fabrics: designers included: Versace, Valentino, Ungaro, Giorgio, Armani etc.

Jason's. 71 New Bond Street, London W1Y 9DE
Tel: 020 7629 2606 Fax: 020 7493 8153

JOHN HEATHCOAT & COMPANY LTD

Weavers, knitters, dyers and finishers of fabrics and nets for technical and apparel end uses.

John Heathcoat & Comapny Ltd. Westexe, Tiverton, Devon EX16 5LL
Tel: 01884 254949 Fax: 01884 252897

JOHN LEWIS

Fabrics, trimmings and haberdashery.

For mail order or details of your nearest branch contact:
John Lewis plc. Oxford Street, London W1A 1EX
Tel: 020 7629 7711

JOHN MASON EXPORT LTD

Leather and suede trims.

John Mason Export Ltd. The Tannery, Queensway, Castleton,
Rochdale, Lancashire OL11 2YN
Tel: 01706 632121 Fax: 01706 648232

JUST CRAFTS WHOLESALE LTD

Large selection of lace trimmings, frillings, ribbons, nets, tulle etc. Trade catalogue.

Just Crafts Wholesale. Stitchery House, London Road, Chalford Stroud,
Gloucestershire GL6 8HN
Fax: 01455 886575

JUST FABRICS

Over 2000 fabrics.

Just Fabrics. The Bridwell, Launceston, Cornwall PL15 7YY
Tel: 01566 776279 Fax: 01566 773239

KINGS FABRICS

Cotton gingham/tartans, Japanese acetate satin, silk dupion, polyesters, viscose etc.

Kings Fabrics. 79 Sword Street, Glasgow G31 1EG

KINGS (FUR FABRICS) LTD

Felt, fleece, fur fabrics and jacquards.

Kings (Fur Fabrics) Ltd. Olive Avenue, Long Eaton, Nottingham NG10 1NN
Tel: 0115 972 5671 Fax: 0115 946 2406

KNITWIT (SYMBOL SYSTEMS LTD)

Mail order and retail suppliers of jersey fabrics for menswear and womenswear, lingerie, sportswear, and swimwear. Notions, patterns and patterns related to working with jersey. Fabric club, sewing books and courses.

Knitwit (Symbol Systems Ltd). 60 Bedford Road, Lower Stondon, Henlow SG16 6DZ
Tel: 01462 851584 Fax: 01462 813621

KNITWIT

66 Hermitage Road, Hitchin, Hertfordshire
Tel: 01462 421479

KUREX FABRICS

Stretch fabrics.

Kurtex Fabrics. 38-40 Edwin Street, Daybrook, Nottingham NG5 6AZ
Tel/Fax: 0115 967 0770

LANITIS TEXTILES (U.K.) LTD

Stockists of a wide range of ladies' fashion fabrics: Satins, crêpes, plain and printed georgette, checks and ginghams and many more.

Lanitis Textiles (U.K.) Ltd. 510C Hornsey Road, London N19 3QW
Tel: 020 7263 7533 Fax: 020 7263 7539

LEONS FABRIC SUPERSTORE

Fashion and bridal fabrics.

Leons Fabric Superstore. 419 Barlow Moor Road, Chorlton, Manchester M21 2ER
Tel: 0161 881 7960

LIBERTY

A wide range of fabrics: silks, viscose, paisleys, printed florals, 100% cotton Tana Lawn, Varuna wool collections, fabrics suitable for men's, womenswear and childrenswear. Trimmings, buttons, beads and yarns all available in a wide selection of colours and designs.

Liberty plc. Liberty House, Regent Street, London W1R 6AH
Tel: 020 7573 9584 Fax: 020 7573 9585

LINTON MILL SHOP

Couture tweed fabrics by the metre and matching designer knit yarns.

Linton Mill Shop. Shaddon Mills, Shaddon Gate, Carlisle, Cumbria. CA2 5TZ
Tel: 01228 527569

LINTON TWEEDS LTD

Novelty and fantasy fabrics for Haute Couture and designer ladieswear market.

Linton Tweeds Ltd. Shaddon Mills, Shaddon Gate, Carlisle, Cumbria CA2 5TZ
Tel: 01228 527569 Fax: 01228 512062

MAC CULLOCH & WALLIS (LONDON) LTD

Mail order, wholesale and retail. Fabrics: silk, bridal, tailoring and many more. Trimmings, haberdashery, millinery supplies, specialist embroidery threads etc.

Mac Culloch & Wallis (London) Ltd. 25-26 Dering Street, London WIR OBH
Tel: 020 762 90311 Fax: 020 749 19578

MAPLE TEXTILES

Fabrics for dressmaking, costume, general fabrics, furnishings: novelty prints, brights, general fabrics, dressmaking, craft, and patchwork. Haberdashery and needlework supplies. Wholesale importer and distributor of American novelty craft, print fabrics.

Maple Textiles. 188-190 Maple Road, Penge, London SE20 8HT
Tel: 020 8778 8049 Fax: 020 8659 0075

A. L. MAUGHAN & COMPANY LTD

Leather and suede for all clothing, gloving, handbags and crafts etc. Chamois and metallic leathers, assorted metal fittings, buckles and tools.

A. L. Maughan & Company Ltd. 5-9 Fazakerley Street,
(off Old Hall Street), Liverpool L3 9DN
Tel/Fax: 0151 236 1872

MEARS GHYLL

Mail order fabrics available. Swiss and Dutch fabrics, large specialist bridal department.

Mears Ghyll. Brookhouse Stores, Nr Brookhouse, Lancaster LA2 9JP
Tel: 01524 770437

MESSRS WATTS & COMPANY LTD

Supplier of silk damasks, brocades, wild silks, cloth of gold, trimmings, linens, interlinings and sundries.

Messrs Watts & Company Ltd. 7 Tufton Street, Westminster, London SW1P 3QE
Tel: 020 7222 7169/1978 Fax: 020 7233 1130

MILLCROFT TEXTILES

Wholesalers of all types of wedding fabrics, tiarras, craft fabrics, fabrics for childrenswear and womenswear. Mail order service available.

Millcroft Textiles. Unit 9 Ivanhoe Industrial Estate, Smisby Road,
Ashby-de-la-Zouch, Leicester LE65 2UU
Tel/Fax: 01530 415007

M. J .J. TRIMCRAFT HOUSE

Fabrics and trimmings.

M. J. Trimcraft House. 100 Spring Hall Lane, Halifax HX1 4TW
Tel: 01422 381723 Fax: 01422 381725

FABRICS

NEVTEX

Worldwide mail order supplier of dance, theatrical fabrics, dress nets, knitted fabrics, woven satins and metalics, chiffons, stretch velour and sequin cloth etc. Feathers, and trimmings. Mail order 24 hour delivery available.

Nevtex. PO Box 87, 29 Stoney Street, Nottingham NG1 1LR
Tel: 0115 959 8781 Fax: 0115 950 2687

NIEDIECK

Brilliant velvet corduroy and simulated furs.

Niedieck. Crotty & Campbell Ltd. 63 Margaret Street, London W1N 7FJ
Tel: 020 7580 0332 Fax: 020 7323 5332

OAK CRAFT SUPPLIES

Wholesale haberdashery and fabric suppliers: Fur fabrics, flat pile, sheep curl pile, Coney, craft and embroidery fabrics. Crochet, craft, embroidery and accessories.

Oak Craft Supplies. Unit 3, Thurrock Enterprise Centre, Maidstone Road, Grays, Essex RM17 6NF
Tel: 01375 386892 Fax: 01375 377116

OAK MOUNT MILL SHOP

Dress and curtain fabrics at mill shop prices.

Oak Mount Mill Shop. Wiseman Street, Burnley, Lancashire BB10 1PP
Tel/Fax: 01282 414950

ODDIES TEXTILES

Wholesalers with a vast range of regular dress and furnishing lines including: calico, muslin, polar fleece, fur fabric, gingham, linings, interlinings, polycottons, 100% cottons, wadding and dress nets. Carrying stock of over 75 different qualities.

Oddies Textiles. Unit 3, Bank House, Greenfield Road, Colne, Lancashire BB8 9NL
Tel: 01282 868600 Fax: 01282 871787

PAGDIN DAVIES LTD

Quality Thai, Indian and Chinese silks in a wide colour range always in stock. No minimum order. Discount for students. Friendly service.

Pagdin Davies Ltd. The Croft, Heol-Y-Barna, Pontardulais, Swansea SA4 1HG
Tel: 01792 883654 Fax: 01792 884310

PANDORA'S FABRIC BOX

Mail order and fabric parties. Beautiful co-ordinating 100% American cotton fabric and quilting threads. Large range of pre-printed picture panels.

Pandora's Fabric Box. Holly Trees, Bramham Road, Clifford, Nr Wetherby LS23 6JQ

PARISIENNE FABRICS

Cashmere, silks and other natural fabrics, designer fabrics, designer buttons, interlinings and interfacings. Large SAE for samples. Mail order available.

Parisienne Fabrics. 4 Worsborough Hall, Worsborough, Barnsley, Yorkshire S70 5LN
Tel: 01226 299358

PENELOPE'S FABRICS

A variety of fabrics for dressmakers, patchworkers and embroiderers': silks, cottons, wools and imports. Mail order. Send SAE for samples and catalogue.

Penelope's Fabrics. 54 Langdon Park Road, London N6 5QG
Tel/Fax: 020 8342 9532

P & R FABRICS LTD

Supplier of fabric specialising in cottons, polyester cotton blends, denims, suitable for workwear, sports and leisure, combat, career and fashion wear.

P & R Fabrics Ltd. Wrengate House, 221 Palatine Road, Didsbury, Manchester M20 2EE
Tel: 0161 438 1133 Fax: 0161 438 1022

PENINE OUTDOOR

Mail order suppliers of outdoor fabrics: waterproof breathables, tent fabrics, rucksack fabrics, over 60 colours of fleece, waterproof and sleeping bag fabrics, zips, buckles, cuffing, patterned braid etc. Suppliers for student collections and projects.

Penine Outdoor. Yew Tree Mills, Holmbridge, Huddersfield, West Yorkshire HD7 1NN
Tel: 01484 689100 Fax: 01484 681783

PHEASANT HOUSE

Studio fashion fabrics woven since 1982, using silk, alpaca, lambswool and Shetland wool. Also museum early reproductions. Personal clients only.

Pheasant House. Little Heath Lane, Berkhamstead, Hertfordshire HP4 2RT
Tel: 01442 871485

POINT NORTH LTD

Mail order suppliers of fabrics for outdoor pursuits (sailing, walking, camping etc). High quality polar fleece, breathable waterproofs, ripstop and microfibre fabrics for DIY clothing and equipment. Also webbing, zips, buckles and patterns.

Point North Ltd. Porthdafarch Road, Holyhead, Anglesey LL65 2LP
Tel: 01407 760195

PONGEES LTD

Silk fabric wholesalers. Natural and dyed silk ranges, jacquards, and beaded silks from around the world, available from stock. Mail order welcome.

Pongees Ltd. 28-30 Hoxton Square, London N1 6NN
Tel: 020 7739 9130 Fax: 020 7739 9132 Visit our website: www.pongees.co.uk

THE POUND A YARD SHOP

Vast assortment of dress and curtain fabric.

The Pound A Yard Shop. Bond Street, Dewsbury
Tel: 01924 438966

QUARRY BANK MILLS

Award winning Georgian cotton mill and museum of the cotton industry. A working museum telling the story of King Cotton from bale of raw cotton to bolt of finished cotton. See hand and machine cotton processes, water and steam. A selection of cotton calico, 100% cotton fabrics available for purchase.

Quarry Bank Mills. Quarry Bank Mill Trust (Enterprises) Ltd. Styal, Wilmslow, Cheshire SK9 4LA
Tel: 01625 527468 Fax: 01625 539267

REMNANT HOUSE

Sheeting fabrics, craft fabrics, 100% silk, muslins, curtain linings, PVC, calico, many dress fabrics and many pure silks.

Remnant House. 26 Commercial Street, Harrogate, North Yorkshire HG1 1TY
Tel: 01423 502707 Fax: 01423 507926

REMNANT KINGS EAST LTD

Retail and wholesale fabric merchants with branches throughout Scotland. Beautiful dress fabrics imported directly from the world's finest mills. Curtain fabrics also available.

Remnant Kings East Ltd. 79 Sword Street, Glasgow G31 1EG
Tel: 0141 556 1147

J. M. RUSSELL

Net and mesh fabrics.

J. M. Russell. 622 Bristol Road South, Northfield, Birmingham B31 2JR

SEAWRIGHT DOUGLAS & COMPANY LTD

Authentic Irish linen and fabrics made from natural fibres suitable for skirts, dress, suits etc.

Seawright Douglas & Company Ltd. 48 Avenue Road, Lurgan, Craigavon, Northern Ireland BT66 7BD

SEW SIMPLE

Knitted fabric specialists: sweatshirting, acrylic jersey, polar fleece. Mail order available.

Sew Simple. Unit 47, Smithbrook Kilns, Nr Cranleigh, Surrey GU6 8JJ

SHADES

Suppliers of French square net.

Shades. 57 Candlemass Lane, Beaconsfield, Buckinghamshire

SHAKER

American homespun fabrics.

72-73 Marylebone High Street, London W1M 3AR
Tel: 020 7935 9461 Fax: 020 7935 4157 www.shaker.co.uk

THE SHUTTLE

Retail and wholesale suppliers of fabric including factory clearance lines in fashion furnishing, calico, muslin etc. A wide range of fabrics available from the high street to the exotic.

The Shuttle. Otley Road, Baildon Bridge, Shipley, West Yorkshire BD17 7AA

THE SILK MILL SHOP

Silk fabrics.

The Silk Mill Shop. Anchor Mill, Mossfold Road, Darwen, Lancashire SK14 1LU
Tel: 01254 873333

THE SILK ROUTE

Silk for embroidery, patchwork, quilting and other crafts. Fabric range include: Silk brocades, organzes and dupion etc. Mail order only.

The Silk Route. 32 Wolseley Road, Godalming, Surrey GU7 3EA
Tel: 01483 420544

SILK SHADES

Specialists in all silk and lace fabrics for bridalwear, embroidered silks, guipure ribbon, Chatilly lace and interior fabrics.

Silk Shades. 15-17 Stoney Street, Nottingham NG1 1LP
Tel: 0115 988 1848 Fax: 0115 950 5166

SIR JACOB BEHRENS & SONS LTD

Textile merchant converters for the apparel and the home furnishing industries. Ranges available ex-stock.

Sir Jacob Behrens & Sons Ltd. Newhaven Business Park, Barton Lane, Eccles, Manchester M30 0TH
Tel: 0161 780 1000 Fax: 0161 787 7613

THE SKEP

Designer fabrics, crêpes, American cottons, polycottons, knitting yarns, silk wools. Handmade samples sent on request. All wool fabrics for Jean Muir and other designers made at the mill and available at affordable prices. Mail order on request.

The Skep. Broom Mills, Coal Hill Lane, Farsley, Leeds LS28 7UT
Tel: 0113 2556769

SKOPOS DESIGN LTD

Manufactures flame retardant fabrics, offering end of contract runs and quality seconds direct to the public.

Skopos Design Ltd. Colbeck House, Cheapside Mills, Bradford Road, West Yorkshire WF17 6LZ
Tel: 01924 475756 Fax: 01924 472096

SMUGGLERS BY MAIL ORDER

1,000 + fabrics.

Smugglers by Mail Order. 3 Capstone Place, Ilfracombe, North Devon EX34 9TQ

FABRICS

SOHO SILKS

Dress, theatrical and furnishing fabrics.

Soho Silks. 24 Berwick Street, London W1V 3RF
Tel: 020 7434 3305 Fax: 020 7494 1705

SPECIAL STITCHES

Patterned jersey in popular children's designs, patterned lycras, waterproof and fleece fabrics, velcro and zips etc.

Special Stitches. PO Box 40, Welshpool, Powys SY21 0ZZ
Tel/Fax: 01938 810412

STONE FABRICS & SEWING SURGERY

Specialising in unusual quality dress fabrics, silks, linens, wools, polar fleece etc. Dress patterns, haberdashery, period buttons, tailoring service, sewing classes and mail order welcome.

Stone Fabrics & Sewing Surgery. 97 High Street, Totnes, Devon TQ9 5PB
Tel/Fax: 01803 868608

TESSA MAYNARD

Thai and Indian silk. Many beautiful colours together, prints, checks and embroidered silks. Please send SAE stating type and colours.

Tessa Maynard. Forge House, Tadley RG26 5SA
Tel/Fax: 01635 298294

TEXTILE TRADERS

Indonesian sample packs, pure cotton batik fabrics from Java, Ikat woven, Indonesian cloths and many other beautiful and unusual fabrics available. Textiles and tools direct from Indonesia wooden and copper printing blocks.

Textile Traders. 37 High Street, Bishop's Castle, Shropshire SY9 5BE

VANNERS MILL SHOP

Silk fabrics by the mertre

Vanners Mill Shop. Gregory Street, Sudbury, Suffolk C010 6BC
Tel: 01787 313933

VILLAGE FABRICS

Specialists in 100% cotton from America for patchwork, quilting and clothing. American books and haberdashery available. Mail order service available.

Village Fabrics. 4-5 St. Leonard's Square, Wallingford, Oxfordshire OX10 OAS
Tel: 01491 204010 Fax: 01491 204013

WEBBER FABRICS

Wool mixes, crepe de chine, jerseys, linens, cottons, ginghams and many other fabrics.

Webber Fabrics. 33 Porchester Grove, Boldon, Tyne & Wear NE35 9ND
Tel: 0191 5373073

WESTDALE TEXTILES

Large selection of lace trimmings, frillings, ribbons, nets, tulle etc. Trade catalogue, factory shop.

Westdale Textiles. Stitchery House, London Road,Chalford, Stroud, Gloucestershire GL6 8HN
Tel/Fax: 01455 886575

WHALEYS (BRADFORD) LTD

Many types of natural fibres, silk, cotton linens, wools, canvas and calicos suitable for dyeing, printing and general purpose. Mail order. Major credit cards accepted. Fast and efficient service, overnight delivery service available.

Whaleys (Bradford) Ltd. Harris Court Mills, Great Horton Road, Bradford BD7 4EQ
Tel: 01274 576718 Fax: 01274 521309

WILLOW FABRICS

Over 8000 fabrics and canvases: cottons, linens, hardanger, tapestry and rug canvases, machine embroidery fabrics and many more. No order is too small.

Willow Fabrics. 95 Town Lane, Mobberley, Cheshire WA16 7HH
Tel: 0800 056 7811 Fax: 01565 872239 (24hrs)

WOLFIN TEXTILES LTD

Calico - various weights, muslin, cottons, cotton ticking etc.

Wolfin Textiles Ltd. 64 Great Titchfield Street, London WIP 7AE
Tel: 0207 636 4949 Fax: 0207 580 4724

THE WORLD OF SEWING

5,000 fabrics in stock for dress and crafts. All manufacturers sewing machines on show and in stock. Suppliers to home, office and education authorities.

The World of Sewing. 56-64 Camden Road, Tunbridge Wells, Kent TN1 2QP
Tel: 01892 533188 Fax: 01892 520 810

Z BUTT TEXTILES

Wide range of fabrics.

24 & 94 Brick Lane, London E1 6RL

Remember to mention the **FASHION & TEXTILE INFORMATION DIRECTORY** *When ordering your supplies*

FATEC
FASHION
AND
TEXTILE
EDUCATIONAL
CONSULTANCY

Colour Predictions for
Autumn/Winter 2000/2001

Organic

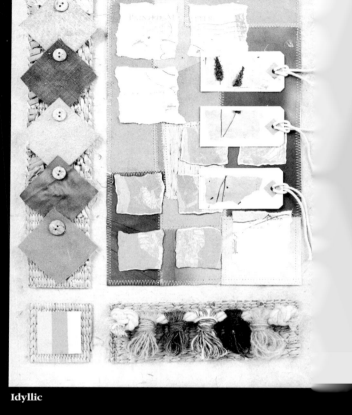

Idyllic

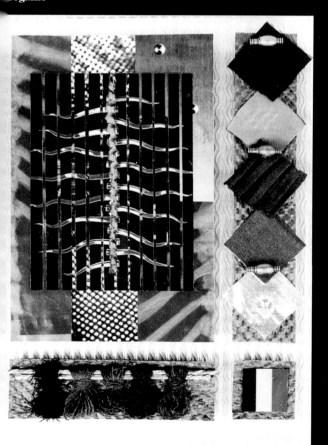

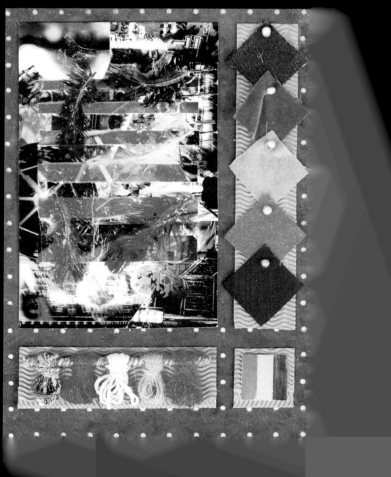

BRITISH LEATHER FASHION COUNCIL

International fashion colour forecasting service.

British Leather Fashion Council. Leather Trade House, Kings Park Road, Moulton Park, Northampton NN3 6JD
Tel: 01604 679999 Fax: 01604 679998

CARLIN (UK) LTD

Producers of publications on forward trends in colour, fabric, yarns etc. (A total of 18 publications) A useful tool for designers in both retail and manufacture.
Design consultancy and trend forecasting agency.

Carlin (UK) Ltd. Richmond House, 419 Richmond Road, Twickenham TW1 2EX
Tel: 020 8296 1860 Fax: 020 8296 1865

THE FASHION SERVICE

Advance fashion trend, colour and information books. CD Rom coverage of designer and couture collection. Designer collection coverage - video and CD Rom facilities.

The Fashion Service. Sue Ryder Richardson. 5 Dryden Street, Covent Garden, London WC2E 9NW
Tel: 020 7829 8300 Fax: 020 7240 5600

ITBD PUBLICATIONS

Fashion forecasting service - fashion and textile publications.

ITBD Publications. 23 Bloomsbury Square, London WC1A 2PJ
Tel: 020 7637 2211 Fax: 020 7637 2248

J. L. PRESENTATIONS

Researcher of market trends, fashion and colours 18 months in advance of the market place. Design and constructs exhibition displays internationally. Photostyling and company identifications.

J. L. Presentations. 5 Grimshaw Street, Burnley, Lancashire BB11 2AX
Tel: 07970 493615 Fax: 01282 450914

MODE INFORMATION LTD

Publisher and distributor of trend, colour and forecasting services, used by major high street retailers and designers.

Mode Information Ltd. First floor, Eastgate House, 16-19 Eastcastle Street, London W1N 7PA
Tel: 020 7436 0133 Fax: 020 7436 0277

SUE RYDER RICHARDSON

Fashion and colour consultant.

Sue Ryder Richardson. 5 Dryden Street, Covent Garden, London WC2E 9NW
Tel: 020 7829 8300 Fax: 020 7240 5600

BOURNE DISPLAYS & SHOPFITTINGS

Suppliers and stockists of a wide range of displays and shopfittings including: garment rails, coat hangers, display busts, hat and shoe stands, jewellery and acrylic displays.
Nationwide delivery service.

Bourne Displays and Shopfittiings. 639 Holloway Road, London N19 5SS
Tel: 020 7272 7870 Fax: 020 7263 0376

BRAITRIM DIRECT

Fashion and retail supplies. Garment covers, polythene covers, packaging materials: bubble wrap, carrier bags, cartons and fancy boxes, adhesive tapes, tissue and craft papers, tickets, labels, pricing sets, rubber stamps, self adhesive labels and tags. Also suppliers of shop stationary, manufacturing, warehouse and stockroom requirements.

Braitrim Direct. Braitrim House, 98 Victoria Road, London NW10 6NB
Tel: 0500 225588 Fax: 020 8723 3003

CARANCO LTD

Leading suppliers of shop and display equipment.

Caranco Ltd. Caranco House, Wilford Road, Nottingham NG2 1EB
Tel: 01602 862272 Fax: 01602 863705

EASTWOOD PLC

Retail trade equipment: shelving, racking, cash registers, counters, dress rails, display signs, security equipment and full range of garment display fittings.

Eastwood PLC. London Works, Ripple Road, Barking, Essex IG11 0SY
Fax: 020 8591 4193

EDEN SHOP EQUIPMENT

Fashion rails of all types, display fittings, hangers, display baskets, display busts etc.
Large showroom. Free mail order catalogue available.

Eden Shop Equipment. 56 Mott Street, Birmingham B19 3HE
Tel: 0121 212 1788 Fax: 0121 212 2583

HANSONS OF LEICESTER

Shop retail fitters.

Hansons of Leicester. 62 Harborough Road, Leicester LE3 0BR
Tel: 0116 255 3330 Fax: 0116 255 3339

K & L GROUP

Retail display equipment, mannequins and tailors dummies.

K & L Group. Crow Road, Romford, Essex RM7 0ES

MILLERS RETAIL DESIGN LTD

Retail display equipment, shop fixtures and fittings.

Millers Retail Display Ltd. Granby house, Greenwood Street, Pendleton, Salford M6 6P2
Tel: 0161 743 1598

MORPLAN

Mail order company supplying over 6,000 products for the fashion and retail industry. Display rails, accessory display, display mannequins and dummies, shop equipment, packing and wrapping items, hangers and size marking and pattern drafting equipment etc.

Morplan. PO Box 54, Harlow, Essex CM20 2TS
Tel: 0800 435 333 Fax: 0800 451928

SPERLING MODELS LTD

Display, retail equipment, mannequins, tailors dummies etc.

Sperling Retail Ltd. 36 Hollands Road, Haverhill, Suffolk CB9 8PR
Tel: 01440 714406 Fax: 01440 714470

TRADE LINES

The complete shopfitting and supply company. Tailors dummies, shelving, hangers, security products, slatboard and accessories, rails, glass cabinets, pegboard fittings and also second hand fittings available.

Trade Lines. 32-34 Constitution Hill, Hockley, Birmingham B19 3JT
Tel: 0121 236 3023 Fax: 0121 233 9960

ADCOPA

Fake suede in 50 colours.

Adcopa. 5 Brookside, Sawtry, Huntingdon, Cambridgeshire PE17 5SB
Tel: 01487 830830 Fax: 01487 832518

A & J FABRICS

Approximately 2000 rolls of upholstery and soft furnishing fabrics. Haberdashery, trimmings, fringing and accessories.

A & J Fabrics. 5 Malthouse Walk, Banbury, Oxon OX16 8PW
Tel: 01295 275550

ABAKHAN FABRIC MILL SHOP

A huge range of remnant fabrics at mill shop prices, including a selection of bridal wear fabrics. 1000's of fabrics from 25p metre, haberdashery, trimmings, soft furnishings fabrics etc. Group discount available. Branches at Mostyn, Liverpool, Birkenhead and Manchester.

Abakhan Fabrics Mill Shop. Coast Road, Mostyn, Flintshire CH8 9DX
Tel: 01745 562100 Fax: 01745 562101

ALMA LEATHER LTD

Stockists of a wide range of leather and suede skins including cow hides, pig suedes, sheepskin, sheep nappa, Mongolian sheepskin, nubucks etc. Retail trade and mail order welcome. Credit cards accepted.

Alma Leather Ltd. Unit D, 12-14 Greatorex Street, London E1 5NF
Tel: 020 7375 0343 Fax: 020 7375 2598

ATRIUM

Simulated leathers and Novasuede in a variety of colours and finishes.

Atrium. Centrepoint, 22-24 St Giles High Street, London WC2H 8LN

BENNETT SILKS

A wonderful selection of silks in every possible colour.

Bennett Silks. Crown Royal Park, Higher Hillgate, Stockport, Cheshire SK1 3HB
Tel: 0161 477 5979 Fax: 0161 480 5385

THE BERWICK STREET CLOTH SHOP

Excellent haunt for a wonderful selection of reasonable priced fabrics.

The Berwick Street Cloth Shop. 15 Berwick Street, London W1V 3RG
Tel: 020 7287 2881

BUTE FABRICS

Unusual fabrics all made from natural fibres, many soft muted tones and luxurious qualities.

Bute Fabrics. Rothesay, Isle of Bute PA20 0DP
Tel: 01700 503734 Fax: 01700 504545

BYWORTH FABRIC WAREHOUSE

Upholstery and furnishing fabrics, haberdashery, trimmings, fringing and accessories.

Byworth Fabric Warehouse. Unit B, Castlefield Industrial Estate, Crossflatts, Bingley, West Yorkshire BD16 2AG
Tel: 01274 561900

CALICO

Plain and printed upholstery fabrics. Many fabrics sold at discounted prices.

Calico. 71-73 City Road, CF2 3BM
Tel: 01222 493020

CLASSIC SILKS

Mail order silks for soft furnishings, bridalwear and eveningwear. 170 plain shades, stripes, tartans, silk dupions, silk mixtures, embroideries, jacquards, sheers, naturals etc. Mail order service.

Classic Silks. 140 Watlington Road, Runcton Holme, Kings Lynn, Norfolk PE33 0EJ
Tel/Fax: 01553 810604

COTSWOLD FABRIC WAREHOUSE

A huge range of upholstery, furnishing fabrics, fringing and trimmings.

Cotswold Fabric Warehouse. 5 Tewkesbury Road, Cheltenham, Gloucestershire GL51 9AH
Tel: 01242 255959

CROFT MILL - J. W. COATES

Fabrics and haberdashery. Sheetings, curtainings, dress fabrics, leisure cloths, silks, lycras available.

Croft Mill - J. W. Coates. Lowther Lane, Foulridge, Colne, Lancashire BB12 9QA
Tel: 01282 869625 Fax: 01282 870038

CROSS FABRICS

Over 2000 rolls of upholstery and soft furnishing fabrics, some clearance lines and seconds, amongst stock fabrics.

Cross Fabrics. Oslo Road, Sutton Fields Estate, Hull, East Riding HU7 0YN
Tel: 01482 879769

THE CURTAIN FABRIC FACTORY SHOP

Curtain fabrics, soft furnishing and upholstery fabrics.

The Curtain Fabric Factory shop. 236A North End Road, Fulham, London W14 9NU
Tel: 020 7381 1777

DESIGNER FABRIC OUTLET

A wide selection of upholstery, furnishing fabrics, haberdashery, trimmings etc.

Designer Fabric Outlet. Birchwood Way, Somercotes, Derbyshire DE55 4Q0
Tel: 01773 602555

DESIGNER'S GUILD
A vast array of Tricia Guilds richly coloured fabrics.

Designer's Guild. 267-271 Kings Road, London SW3 5EN
Tel: 020 7243 7300 Fax: 020 7243 7710

A. DUNNICLIFF
Quality leathers, mixed colour bags, large pieces available.

A. Dunnicliffe. Tree Tops, Calke Road, Melbourne, Derby DE73 1DL

ESSEX FABRIC WAREHOUSE
A vast range of upholstery and furnishing fabrics, voiles, velvets, damasks, cottons, linens, calicos, nets, jacquards etc.

Essex Fabric Warehouse. Unit 2, Sainbury's Homebase, London Road, Vange, Basildon, Essex SS16 4PR
Tel: 01268 552224

THE FABRIC CORNER
An enormous range of soft furnishing fabrics: plains, prints, cottons, voiles, muslins, damasks etc. Many designer names available.

The Fabric Corner. Market Street Centre. Market Street, South Normanton, Derbyshire DE55 2AB
Tel: 01773 863700

THE FABRIC WAREHOUSE
Upholstery and soft furnishing fabrics.

The Fabric Warehouse. 52 Fore Street, Redruth, Cornwall TR15 2AF
Tel: 01209 314439

FABRIC WORLD
Large ranges of upholstery, soft furnishing and dress fabrics - 3000 bolts selling from £4.99-£20 metre. Normally sold at double the price.

Fabric World. 287-289 High Street, Sutton, Surrey SM1 1LL
Tel: 020 8643 5127 Fax: 020 8770 0021

FACTORY FABRIC WAREHOUSE
A wide range of upholstery, soft furnishing fabrics, trimmings and accessories.

Factory Fabric Warehouse. Units 4-5, Roundswell Industrial Estate, Barnstaple, Devon EX32 9DD
Tel: 01271 327755

FACTORY FABRIC WAREHOUSE
Voiles, cotton satins, damasks, velvets, chintzes, brocades, moires, dralons, vinyls, tapestries, linens, calico, jacquards, cottons for soft furnishing and upholstery.

Factory Fabric Warehouse. 40-42 Regent Street, Clifton, Bristol BS8 2XP
Tel: 0117 970 6512

THE FACTORY FABRIC WAREHOUSE

Large range of upholstery and soft furnishing fabrics, haberdashery, trimmings, remnants, discontiued lines, seconds and roll ends.

The Factory Fabric Warehouse. 1 Bridgeford Road, off Trusham Road, Marsh Barton Trading Estate, Exeter EX2 8QX Tel: 01392 422881
Contact Freephone: 0800 699899 for your nearest Factory Fabric Warehouse.

FIRED EARTH

Extensive range of timeless fabrics and shaker cottons. Quality interior finishes. Catalogue available.

Fired Earth. Twyford Mill, Oxford Road, Adderbury, Oxon OX17 3HP
Tel: 01295 812088 Fax: 01295 810832

FREELANCE FABRICS

A wide range of soft furnishing and upholstery fabrics: nets, calicos, cottons, damasks, voiles, linens, accessories, trimmings and haberdashery available.

Freelance Fabrics. 1-3 Hancock Drive, Bushmead Road, Luton, Bedfordshire LU2 7SF
Tel: 01582 411522 Freephone: 0800 699899 for your nearest store.

IAN MANKIN

Utility fabrics - stripes, tickings, plains and over 300 different natural fabrics. Mail order available.

Ian Mankin. 109 Regents Park Road, London NW1 8UR
Tel: 020 7722 0997

JUST FABRICS

A wide range of upholstery and furnishing fabrics, stocking all the leading brands and names in interior fabric design.

Just Fabrics. The Bridwell, Dockacre Road, Launceston, Cornwall PL15 8YY
Tel: 01566 776279 Fax: 01566 773239

KNICKERBEAN

Knickerbean has 5 main branches: Bath, Bury St Edmunds, Newbury, St. Albans and Tunbridge Wells stocking many designer name fabrics at bargain prices. Soft furnishing, upholstery, accessories and haberdashery available.

Knickerbean. Tel: 01842 751327 for branch details.

LOW WOODS FURNISHINGS

An enormous range of curtain and upholstery designer fabrics
- discontinued lines and quality seconds

Low Woods Furnishings. Low Woods Lane, Belton, Shepshed, Leicestershire LE12 9TP
Tel: 01530 222246

MAUREEN WHITMORE FINE FURNISHINGS

Soft furnishing accessories and equipment available including fabrics supplied to all small businesses at competitive prices. Special courses arranged for workrooms, showing professional techniques and short-cuts to perfection.

Maureen Whitmore Fine Furnishings. Old Church Hotel, Watermillock, Penrith, Cumbria CA11 0JN
Tel: 01768 486272 Fax: 01768 486368

MIDLAND FABRIC WAREHOUSE

A wide stock of soft furnishing fabrics.

Midland Fabric Warehouse. Units 2 & 3 Oak Park, Dudley Road,
Stourbridge Area, Brierley Hill DY5 1HR
Tel: 01384 482424

THE MILL FABRIC SHOP

Designer fabrics at discount prices: cottons, chintz, satins, jacquards and damasks etc.

The Mill Shop. Cartwright Street, Newton, Hyde SK14 4QU
Tel: 0161 367 9337

THE NATURAL FABRIC COMPANY.

Retail and mail order service available, supplying a wonderful range of natural fabrics: silks, cottons, linens, wools, hessian's, chambray, damask tickings, calicos and many other interesting fabrics.

The Natural Fabric Company. Wessex Place, 127 High Street,
Hungerford, Berkshire RG17 0DL
Tel: 01488 684002 Fax: 01488 686455

ODDIES TEXTILES

Wholesalers with a vast range of regular dress and furnishing lines including: calico, muslin, polar fleece, fur fabric, gingham, linings, cottons, wadding etc.

Oddies Textiles. Unit 3, Bank House, Greenfield Road, Colne, Lancashire BB8 9NL
Tel: 01282 868600 Fax: 01282 871787

THE ORIGINAL SILVER LINING COMPANY

Linings, muslins, calico, cottons, cotton sheetings, lawns etc.

The Original Silver Lining Company. Workshop 29, Lenton Business Centre,
Lenton Boulevard, Nottingham NG7 2BY
Tel: 0115 955 5123

RED ROSE FABRICS LTD

Manufacturers of cotton velvets, viscose, polyesters and other fabrics for upholstery, soft furnishings and fashion. Top quality tailoring fabrics, printed velvets, all woven on site.

Red Rose Fabrics Ltd. Royal Mill, Victoria Street, Accrington, Lancashire BB5 0PG
Tel: 01254 392059 Fax: 01254 385070

SANDERSON

Manufacturers and retailers of a wide range of their own fabrics as well as a good range of designer names. Cottons, velvets, prints and plains.

Sanderson. 112-120 Brompton Road, London SW3 1JJ
Tel: 020 7584 3344 Fax: 020 7584 3344 (contact for your nearest stockists)

SEWING PARADISE

Seconds in furnishing, upholstery and dress fabrics.

Sewing Paradise. 142 East Reach, Taunton, Somerset TA6 4SL
Tel: 01823 276861

SHAKER

American Shaker homespun cloth.

Shaker. 72-73 Marylebone High Street, London W1M 3AR
Tel: 020 7935 9461 Fax: 020 7935 4157

SILK SHADES

Silks for soft furnishings and upholstery: plain, patterned, tartans, stripes and embroidered fabrics.

Silk Shades. 8 Water Street, Lavenham, Suffolk C010 9RW
Tel: 01787 247029

SIR JACOB BEHRENS & SONS LTD

Textile merchant converters for the apparel and home furnishing industries. Ranges available ex-stock.

Sir Jacob Behrens & Sons Ltd. Newhaven Business Park, Barton Lane, Eccles, Manchester M30 0TH
Tel: 0161 780 1000 Fax: 0161 787 7613

SOHO SILKS

Furnishing, dress and theatrical fabrics.

Soho Silks. 24 Berwick Street, London W1V 3RF
Tel: 020 7434 3305 Fax: 020 7494 1705

WARWICK FABRICS CLEARANCE SHOP

Furnishing fabrics - plains and patterns, chintz, cottons, cotton satins, jacquards. Many discounted lines at excellent prices.

Warwick Fabrics Clearance Shop. Hackling House, Industrial Park, Bourton-on-the-Water, Gloucestershire GL54 2EN
Tel: 01451 820772

WHARF MILL TEXTILES

A wide range of soft furnishing and curtaining fabrics.

Wharf Mill Textiles. Caroline Street, Wigan, Lancashire WN3 4EZ
Tel: 01942 825352 Fax: 01942 825322

WOLFIN TEXTILES LTD

Various weight calicos, muslin, cottons, cotton ticking and utility fabrics.

Wolfin Textiles Ltd. 64 Great Tichfield Street, London W1P 7AE
Tel: 020 7636 4949 Fax: 020 7580 4724

YARNOLDS

Soft furnishing and curtain fabrics - discontinued lines and remnants available.

Yarnolds. 106 Birmingham Road, Wolverhampton, West Midlands WV2 3NZ
Tel: 01902 459321

CLEARBOX

Clear boxes to order, supplied flat. Small or large quantities. Any size.

Clearbox. 5 Trdyson Place, Falmouth, Cornwall TR11 2RH
Tel: 01326 314661

CLWYD PHOTOSERVICES

Self adhesive colour photos "label prints" in 3 sizes.

Clwyd Photoservices. 2A Ryeland Street, Shotton, Deeside, Clwyd CH5 1DT
Tel: 0800 542 7589

CONELLA LTD (Staples Group)

Labels - woven and printed. Comprehensive catalogue available.

Conella Ltd. (Staples Group), Lockwood Road, Huddersfield HD1 3QW
Fax: 01484 434993

CREATION CARRIERS

Suppliers of paper and polythene carrier bags - all types, printed and plain, labels, swing tags, garment covers and packaging materials.

Creation Carriers. 201 Feltham Hill Road, Ashford, Middlesex TW15 1HJ
Tel: 01784 248800 Fax: 01784 248866

DIVERSE MARKETING

High wash resistant fabric labels. Specialist short and medium runs, quantities from 100. Also size and fibre content labels. Catalogue and samples available.

Diverse Marketing. Bannachra Studios, Blairmore, Nr Dunoon, Argyll PA23 8TL
Tel: 01369 840543

EVE BULL LABELS

Mail order supplier of fabric labels with attractive embroidered designs, suitable for adults and childrens garment. Small quantities supplied.

Eve Bull Labels. Long Dyke, The Drive, Chichester, Sussex PO15 4QA
Tel: 01243 527280

INDEX (PLASTICS) LTD

Polythene bags, packaging, self adhesive hooks, polypropylene bags and easi-slide wallets. Most hooks are available from stock with most bags being produced to order.

**Index (Plastics) Ltd. 3 Onslow Close, Kingsland Business Park,
Basingstoke, Hampshire RG24 8QL**

KALEIDOSCOPE SUPPLIES

Bags, carriers, tissue bubble wraps, labels, swing tags, retail tickets, bags etc.

Kaleidoscope Supplies. North Street, Langport, Somerset TA10 9RQ
Tel: 01458 253631 Fax: 01458 252655

LEA LABELS

Mail order supplier of printed fabric garment labels. Specialist short run quantities (from 50) for the craft, garment market, including size and fibre content label.

Lea Labels. PO Box 30, Cromer, Norfolk NR27 0NL
Tel/Fax: 01263 579289

MINILABEL

Address labels, brochure available.

Minilabel. Finches Yard, Mill Green Road, Haywards Heath, West Sussex RH16 1XQ
Tel: 01444 417259 Fax: 01444 417259

MORPLAN

Mail order company supplying over 6,000 products for the fashion and retail industry.

Display rails, accessory display, display mannequins and dummies, shop equipment, packaging and wrapping: labels, tapes and dispensers, sales tickets, tag attachments and tag guns, promotional tickets, bubble wrap, wrapping items etc.

Morplan. PO Box 54, Harlow, Essex CM20 2TS
Tel: 0800 435 333 Fax: 0800 451928

NATIONAL WEAVING

Manufacturers of woven name tapes and short run custom design labels with minimum 500 run. Short run personalised woven labels.

National Weaving. Redstone Mills, Narberth, Pembrokeshire SA67 7ES
Tel: 01834 861446 Fax: 01834 861757

NOR SYSTEMS LTD

Data capture systems and labelling. Barcode printers, scanners and software with a complete range of tags, tickets and self adhesive labels.

Nor Systems Ltd. Valley Road, Harwich, Essex CO12 4RR
Tel: 01255 240000 Fax: 01255 241111

OVERSOLVE LTD

Manufacturers of both polythene and paper carriers in a variety of sizes and colours from 1000 upwards, fast turn around and full in-house design facilities.

Oversolve Ltd. Units 8, Salisbury Square, Radford, Nottingham NG7 2AB
Tel: 0115 9424840 Fax: 0115 9424841

PROTEC

Packaging supplies: Bubblewrap, tissue, brown wrapping, film fronted and strong plastic bags for small and medium size businesses. Discounts on orders of over £100.

Protec. 62 Windermere Avenue, Wembley, Middlesex, London HA9 8RY
Tel: 020 8908 4601

TERRY ANDREWS (t/a THE BAG N' BOX MAN)

Large stock of boxes and bags supplied in almost any quantity throughout the British Isles. Custom made service also available. Fax for catalogue.

Terry Andrews. Unit 1, West Street, Shutford, Banbury, Oxon OX15 6PH
Tel: 01295 788522 Fax: 01295 788523

VIKING DIRECT LTD

Warehouse and packaging supplies. Sealing and transparent tapes, printed and personalised packaging tapes, cartons, stock boxes, bubble wrap, etc.

Viking Direct Ltd. Bursom Industrial Park, Tollwell Road, Leicester LE4 1BR
Tel: 0800 424445 Fax: 0800 622211

WILLERINGHAUS & COMPANY LTD

Printed and woven garment labels, swing tickets, embroidered badges and PVC packaging. Send sketch or fax us for quote by return.

Willeringhaus & Company Ltd. The Mill, 23 Saunderts Copse, Mayford, Woking, Surrey GU22 0NS
Tel/Fax: 01483 723158

WRIGHTSONS BRITISH TAGS LTD

Manufacturers and suppliers of garment labelling and printed packaging. Products include: woven, printed and self adhesive labels, swing tickets, plastic carrier bags.

Wrightsons British Tags Ltd. Tagwright House, 35-41 Westland Place, London N1 7LS
Tel: 020 7253 2350 Fax: 020 7490 1193

ANNA'S LACE CHEST

Crochet, bobbin lace, needle lace, lace knitting and tape lace. Mail order service. Catalogue available on request.

Anna's Lace Chest. 1 Gorse Close, Whitehills, Northampton NN2 8ED
Tel: 01604 461536

BARTLETT, CAESAR & PARTNERS

Lace equipment and makers of lace bobbins.

Bartlett, Caesar & Partners. 12 Creslow Court, Galley Hill, Stony Stratford, Buckinghamshire MK11 1NN
Tel: 01908 262388

BRIDAL LACES & SILK FABRICS

Mail order, trade and retail. Catalogue and map available.

Bridal Laces & Silk Fabrics. Leopold Street, Long Eaton, Nottingham NG10 4QE
Tel: 0115 946 0766 Fax: 0115 946 0741

BRIDAL LACES & FABRICS

Extensive range of fabrics and bridal laces. Trade and retail suppliers to the bride herself, to the designer, dressmaker, supplier throughout Europe.

Bridal Laces & Fabrics. 28 Stoney Street, The Lace Market, Nottingham NG1 1LL
Tel/Fax: 0115 958 6695

E & J PIPER

Silk embroidery and lace thread.

E & J Piper. Silver Lea, Flax Lane, Glemsford, Suffolk C010 7RS

HONITON LACE

Fine antique lace, bridal lace and wedding veils, lace making equipment and books. Mail order and wholesale.

Honiton Lace. 44 High Street, Honiton, Devon EX14 8PJ
Tel: 01404 42416 Fax: 01404 47797

JO FIRTH

Lace making and needlecraft suppliers. All lace making equipment including pins, threads, pillows, bobbins, books, delicia beads, wires and accessories, also needlelace, tatting requirements and embroidery equipment.

Jo Firth. 58 Kent Crescent, Lowtown, Pudsey, West Yorkshire LS28 9EB
Tel: 0113 257 4881

LACE GUILD

To promote the study, collecting and use of lace.

The Lace Guild. The Hollies, 53 Audnam, Stourbridge, West Midlands DY8 4AE
Tel: 01384 390739 Fax: 01384 444415

LACE CENTRE

Founded in 1980 by eight leading lace manufacturers. The Lace Centre has a wide choice of styles and prices in genuine, quality Nottingham Lace. Open seven days a week. Postal service available.

Lace Centre. Severn's Building, Castle Road, Nottingham NG1 6AA
Tel: 0115 941 3539

MAINLY LACE

Threads, bobbins, bobbin lace, tatting and crochet, also hand made lace and small lace motifs. Mail order service.

Mainly Lace. Moulsham Mill, Parkway, Chelmsford CM2 7PX
Tel: 01245 608200

NEWHAM LACE EQUIPMENT

Lace making equipment

Newham Lace Equipment. 15 Marlowe Close, Basingstoke, Hampshire RG24 9DD

NOTTINGHAM LACE CENTRE

Specialists in all types of Nottingham Lace ie: edgings, trimmings, wedding laces etc.

Nottingham Lace Centre. Victoria Market, Victoria Centre, Nottingham NG1 3PP
Tel: 0115 941 4058

ROSE'S MILL

Traditional Nottingham lace.

Rose's Mill. 76 Cowbridge Road East, Canton, Cardiff, CF1 9DW
Tel: 01222 667201 Fax: 01222 703690

SPANGLES

Mail order and retail and wholesale. Beads, beading equipment and beading books. Retail lacemaking bobbins.

Spangles. 1 Casburn Lane, Burwell, Cambridge CB5 0ED
Tel/Fax: 01638 742024

STEF FRANCIS

Linen threads for lace work.

Stef Francis. Waverley, Higher Rocombe, Newton Abbot, Devon TQ12 4QL
Tel/Fax: 01803 323004

STITCHES & LACE

A wide range of items for lacemakers, cross stitchers, patchworkers and quilters: books, bobbins, threads, German linens, cottons, silks, rayon threads, fabrics, charts. Mail order catalogue available. Lace museum with replica lacemakers cottage.

Stitches & Lace. Alby Craft Centre, Cromer Road, Alby, Norwich, Norfolk NR11 7QE
Tel: 01263 768002

WESTDALE LACE AND EMBROIDERY SUPPLIES

Threads, lace, charts and kits.

Westdale Lace and Embroidery Supplies. Yvonne Close, Orchid Cottage, Drury Lane, Mortimer Common, Reading RG7 2JN
Tel: 01089 332670 Fax: 01189 331490

WESTDALE TEXTILES

Large selection of lace trimmings, frillings, ribbons, nets, tulle etc.
Trade catalogue and factory shop.

Westdale Textiles. Stitchery House, Chalford, Stroud, Gloucestershire GL6 8HN
Tel/Fax: 01453 886575

Discover lace and the history behind it at...

The Museum of Nottingham Lace

◆ Hear the story of lace from the workers and inventors

◆ Working lace machine demonstrations * (limited hours)

◆ Costumes and examples of lace

◆ Handling collection

◆ Videos of the industry - past and present

◆ Self-guided audio tour of The Lace Market area

◆ **The** historical resource centre for Nottingham Lace

◆ Group bookings have discounted admission

3-5 High Pavement, The Lace Market,

Nottingham, NG1 1HF

Tel: 0115 989 7365 Fax: 0115 989 7301

e-mail: lacemuseum@innotts.co.uk

ANGLO - AMERICAN SEWING MACHINES COMPANY LTD

Industrial sewing machines, cloth cutting machines, electric motors, spare parts, labour saving attachments, sewing machine needles etc.

Anglo - American Sewing Machine Company Ltd. 1-5 Waterson Street, London E2 8HE
Tel: 020 7739 5847/8 Fax: 020 7729 6648

ANNA CRUTCHLEY - PASSEMENTERIE

Cord twister for spinning fine twines and chucky cords, ensuring quality twists which can be used for split-ply braiding.

Anna Crutchley - Passementerie. The Frater Studio, 6B Priory Road, Cambridge CB5 8HT
Tel: 01223 327685

BABYLOCK SEWING MACHINES

Blind hemmers and baby lockers. Colour brochure available.

Babylock Sewing Machines. Murdock Road, Bedford MK41 7LE
Tel: 01234 363433

BAMBERS OF MANCHESTER

The worlds best machines: Bernina, Janome, Brother, Elna, Pfaff, Passap, Horn, Toyota available from our showroom. Catalogue available. Please send for details.

Bambers of Manchester. 42-44 Oldham Street, Manchester M4 1LE
Tel: 0161 236 0129

BOGOD MACHINE COMPANY LTD

Sewing machines and accessories.

Bogod Machine Company Ltd. 50-52 Great Sutton Street, London EC1 0DJ
Tel: 020 7253 1198 Fax: 020 7250 0016

BRI-STOR SYSTEMS LTD

Portabox - equipment storage containers.

Bri-stor Ltd. Hixon, Stafford ST18 0PF
Tel: 01889 271202

BROMLEY SEWING MACHINES

Sewing machines and accessories.

Bromley Sewing Machines. 54-56 Camden Road, Tonbridge Wells, Kent TN1 2QP

BROTHER UK LTD

A manufacturer and supplier of sewing machinery to the garment/ clothing industries and allied trades supported by after sales service. Spare part supplier.

Brother UK Ltd. Shepley Street, Guide Bridge, Audenshaw, Manchester M34 5JD
Tel: 0161 931 2240 Fax: 0161 931 2211

COUNTY SEWING MACHINES

Sewing machines and overlockers, sales, service and repairs. Bernina, Viking, Husqvarna, New Home, Janome, Bernette etc. Supplier to educational establishments.

County Sewing Machines. 74 Westgate, Grantham, Lincolnshire NG35 6LA
Tel: 01476 564267

CRUISEVALE LTD

Retail sale - parts and repairs of industrial sewing machines. All makes catered for. Also suppliers of all cutting room equipment including all cutting room papers.

Cruisevale Ltd. 15C Osborn Street, London E1 6TD
Tel: 020 7247 4168 Fax: 020 247 0559

H. CUBITT BEXFIELD LTD

Specialist supplier of scissors and shears.

H. Cubitt Bexfield Ltd. Mundial House, Kiveton Park Station,
Kiveton Park, Sheffield S26 6NP
Tel: 01909 772866 Fax: 01909 773410

DAVID DRUMMOND

Sewing machine specialist.

David Drummond. 79-81 Haymarket Terrace, Edinburgh EH12 5HD
Tel: 0131 539 7766

DAYLIGHT STUDIOS LTD

Specialises in magnifying lamps for the sewing industry, low heat, no colour distortion, enhancing lights along with a range of magnifying aids. Daylight bulbs and tubes, lamps and magnifyers, visual accessories.

Daylight Studios Ltd. 89-91 Scrubs Lane, London NW10 6QU
Tel: 020 8964 1300

DISCOUNT LIGHTING LTD

Discount lighting specialises in the production of low heat halogen enhancer lights for sewing, along with magnifying aids. They have a full mail order service. Brochure is available on request, or check out their web site on www.halogen-lights.demon.co.uk

Discount Lighting Ltd. 32 Gunton Church Lane, Gunton, Lowestoft NR32 4LF
Tel: 01502 587 598 Fax: 01502 514 592

EASTMAN MACHINE COMPANY LTD

General fashion and pattern cutting equipment: rulers, scissors, pattern cutting card, spot and cross pattern cutting paper, grading equipment, art materials and books for the apparel industry.

Eastman Machine Company Ltd. Duro House, Station Estate,
Eastwood Close, London E18 1BY
Tel: 020 8989 7784

E. L. GRAIN SEWING MACHINES LTD

Scissors, shears, sewing and embroidery machines, sewing needles, machine parts and accessories.

E. L. Grain Sewing Machines Ltd. Highcross Street, Nottingham, NG1 3AX
Tel: 0115 947 5638 Fax: 0115 948 4067

ELNA SEWING MACHINES (GB) LTD

418 Chester Road, Boldmere, Sutton Coldfield, West Midlands B73 5EB
Tel: 0121 373 5497

EMBERFERN LTD

Suppliers of cutroll strip cutters and checkroll and checkmaster fabric inspection and measuring equipment. Cappa sample cutters and pinking shears.

Emberfern Ltd. 25 Westgate, Otley, West Yorkshire LS21 3AT
Tel: 01943 46755 Fax: 01943 850362

FAÇADES

Supplier of specialist furniture.

Façades. Graphic House, Horsepond Meadow, South Moulton, Devon EX36 4EJ

R. D. FRANKS LTD

Superb range of fashion and textile periodicals and books. Table top equipment, tailors' models, mail order available all around the world. Shop opening times Mon - Fri 9 am - 5 pm.

R. D. Franks Ltd. Kent House, Market Place (off Titchfield Lane), Oxford Circus, London W1N 8EJ (nearest tube station Oxford Circus)
Tel: 0207 636 1244 Fax: 0207 436 4904

FREUDENBERG NONWOVENS LP

Manufacturers of nonwoven interfacings, fusible interfacings - vilene, iron-on edge tape, high bulk volume fleece, shoulder pads, sewing aids, craft and soft furnishing products etc.

Freudenberg Nonwovens LP. Vilene Retail. Lowfields Business Park, Elland, West Yorkshire HX5 5DX
Tel: 01422 327900 Fax: 01422 327950

FRISTER & ROSSMAN SEWING MACHINES LTD

Sewing machines.

Frister & Rossman Sewing Machines Ltd. Mark Way, Swanley, Kent BR8 8NG

B. HAGUE & COMPANY LTD

Hague manufacturer and supplier of domestic and industrial linking machines, winders, machine knitting accessories, plus many other aids for machine knitters, which can be obtained by mail order.

B. Hague & Company Ltd. 45 Mile End Road, Colwick, Nottingham NG4 2DW
Tel: 0115 987 0031 Fax: 0115 987 290

HEART OF ENGLAND SEWING MACHINES

Supply, service and training in the use of computer sewing machines to schools and businesses. Mail order textile supplies and haberdashery. Multi cultural supplies for schools and colleges.

Heart of England Sewing Machines. 9 Alveston Grove, Knowle, Solihull, West Midlands B93 9NT
Tel: 01564 772156 Fax: 01564 777801

HORN FURNITURE (UK) LTD

Supplier of specialist sewing machine furniture for eighty years. The range of furniture is designed to accommodate all makes of domestic sewing machines.

Horn Furniture (UK) Ltd. Unit 2, Brookwood Industrial Estate, Brookwood Avenue, Eastleigh, Hampshire SO50 9EY
Tel: 01703 642308 Fax: 01703 610742

HOUSE OF SMOCKING

Mail order supplier of smocking pleaters, patterns, books, transfer dots and all smocking needs. Callers welcome by appointment.

House of Smocking. 1 Ryeworth Road, Charlton Kings, Cheltenham, Gloucestershire GL52 6LG
Tel: 01242 245204

HUSQVARNA VIKING SEWING MACHINES

Swedish sewing machine manufacturer of embroidery computerised and electronic domestic machines. Also supplier of embroidery software packages and sewing machine accessories.

Husqvarna Viking Sewing Machines. Viking House, Cheddar Industrial Park, Wedmore Road, Cheddar. BS27 3EB
Tel: 01934 744533 Fax: 01934 744811

JANOME UK LTD

Sewing accessories, scissors, pinking and tailoring shears etc.

Janome UK Ltd. Janome Centre, Southside, Bredbury, Stockport, Cheshire SK6 2SP
Tel: 0161 666 6011

JOHNSONS SEWING AND KNITTING MACHINES

Sewing, knitting machines and accessories.

Johnsons Sewing and Knitting Machines. 22 Wood Street, Doncaster, South Yorkshire DN1 3LW
Tel: 01302 369777

KENNETT & LINDSELL LTD

Design & manufacturer of industrial tailors' dummies for the clothing industry and education. Pattern grading equipment, stock shapes and custom specifications.

Kennett & Lindsell Ltd. Crow Lane, Romford, Essex RM7 OES
Tel: 01708 749732 Fax: 01708 733328

KINROSS (SUPPLIES)

Stockists of polycotton and polyester sewing industrial type sewing threads for overlocking and lockstitch machines, supplying home dressmakers and small units through mail order

Kinross (Supplies). PO Box 55, Pinner HA5 4UL
Tel: 020 8421 1685

LIN & NIGEL MASON FURNITURE

The sit kneel chair.

Lin & Nigel Mason Furniture. 22 Wood Street, Doncaster, South Yorkshire DN1 3LW
Tel: 01588 620101

MORPLAN LTD

Clothing, manufacture and pattern cutting/grading equipment, portfolios, specialist books, scissors, shears, threads and art equipment.

Morplan Ltd. PO Box 54, Temple Bank, Harlow, Essex CM20 2YB
Tel: 0800 435 333 Fax: 0800 451 928

OSWALDTWISTLE MILLS

Embroidery machines and accessories, sewing machines and overlockers, furnishing fabrics and remnant shop.

Oswaldtwistle Mills. Oswaldtwistle, Accrington, Lancashire
Tel: 01254 389171

PASSAP

Machines and accessories.

Passap. Bogod Machine Company Ltd. 50-52 Great Sutton Street, London EC1 ODJ
Tel: 020 7253 1198 Fax: 020 7250 0016

POLDY LTD

Button covering machinery.

Poldy Ltd. Unit 19, Hallmark Trading Centre, Fourth Way, Wembley, Middlesex HA9 0LB
Tel/Fax: 020 8795 5007

PROPORTIONS

Dress stands.

Proportions. 2-4 Old Street, London EC1

PROSHARP

Sharpening Services and tool sales. All inclusive sharpening and replacement of scissors, knives and woodworking and craft tooling. All trades and professions use PROSHARP.

Prosharp. 29 Prospect Place, Hayle, Cornwall TR27 4LU
Tel/Fax: 01736 756162

SEWING WORLD

Sewing machines, overlockers, sales, services and accessories. A wide range of haberdashery, dressmaking and craft patterns, paper patterns - mail order available

Sewing World. 308-310 Wimborne Road, Winton Banks, Bournemouth, Dorset BH9 2HN
Tel: 01202 528451 Fax: 01202 775590

SEWMASTER SEWING MACHINES

Main agents for Bernina, Pfaff Husqvarna, Brother. Sales, services and spares.

Sewmaster Sewing Machines. 3 West Street, Reading, Berkshire RG1 1TT
Tel: 0118 957 1845 Fax: 0118 957 1603

SINGER SERVICES

Regional Service Centre, repairing sewing machines, overlockers etc. New and conditioned sewing machines - domestic and industrial - overlockers, presses and machine accessories.

Singer Services. 77 Coleman Road, Leicester LE5 4LE
Tel: 0116 274 2681 Fax: 0116 246 0925

SINGER (UK) LTD

Machines and accessories.

Singer (UK) Ltd. 91 Coleman Road, Leicester LE5 4LE

STAPLES GROUP PLC

Manufacture paper, spot and cross, haberdashery, trimmings, hooks and eyes, shoulder pads, interfacings, fusables, velcro, waistbands, garment bags, hangers etc.

Staples Group PLC. Lockwood Road, Huddersfield, West Yorkshire HD1 3QW
Tel: 01484 88 88 88 Fax: 01484 88 88 00

TOYOTA SEWING AND KNITTING MACHINES

Machines and accessories.

Toyota Sewing and Knitting Machines. 34 High Street, Bromley, Kent BR1 1EA

VIKING SEWING MACHINES LTD t/a HUSQVARNA

Swedish manufacturer of domestic sewing machines, overlockers, embroidery software and sewing machine accessories. Products can be purchased through authorised stockists.

Viking Sewing Machines Ltd. Viking House, Cheddar Business Park, Wedmore Road, Cheddar, Somerset BS27 3EB
Tel: 01934 744533 Fax: 01934 744811

BAXTER HART AND ABRAHAM LTD

Complete millinery suppliers: hat trimmings, petersham ribbon, wool felts, hat stiffeners, buchram, feathers and accessories etc. Mail order and price list available.

Baxter Hart & Abraham Ltd. 141 New Bedford Road, Luton LU3 1LF
Tel: 01582 721381 Fax: 01582 405726

F. BECK LTD

Manufacturers of braids, buttons, frogging, trimmings and accessories.
UK agents for Menoni, metal components.

F.Beck Ltd. 402 Harrow Road, London W9 2HU
Tel: 020 7286 9951 Fax: 020 7266 3391

BOON & LANE LTD

Aluminium and wood hat blocks. Suppliers of blocking machines, hat stretchers, equipment and accessories.

Boon & Lane Ltd. 7-11 Taylor Street, Luton, Bedfordshire LU2 OEY
Tel: 01582 723224 Fax: 01582 402298

BOURNE'S DISPLAYS & SHOPFITTINGS

Hat stands and display forms (foam, plastic and polished wood heads).

Bourne's Display. 639 Holloway Road, London N19 5SS
Tel: 020 7272 7870 Fax: 020 7236 0376

CATHERINE DELANEY

Suppliers of millinery materials, theatre, television and special occasion milliner. Blocking service available. Exclusive hats made to order.

Catherine Delaney. Unit 006, The Chandlery, 50 Westminster Bridge Road, London SE1 7QY
Tel: 020 7721 7623 Fax: 020 7721 7409 www.catherinedelaney.co.uk

W. FISCHER & SONS (LUTON).

Hat trimmings and accessories.

W.Fischer & Sons (Luton) Ltd. 4A William Street, Luton LU22 7RE
Tel: 01582 404022 Fax: 01582 400455

FLOWERS BY NOVELTY LTD

Manufacturer and importers of artificial flowers for millinery, clothing, trimming, decorating and accessories etc.

Flowers By Novelty. Unit 1, Mill Lane, Fullbridge, Maldon, Essex CM9 4NX
Tel: 01621 854981 Fax: 01621 858761

GUY MORSE-BROWN

Hat blocks, hat stretchers and accessories by mail order. Specials designed and made to your requirements. Free fully illustrated catalogue. Visit our website at www.hatblocksz.co.uk

Guy Morse-Brown. Mill Lane Farm House, Mill Lane, Wombourne, Staffordshire WV5 OLE
Tel/Fax: 01902 893683

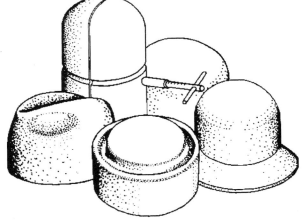
THE HAT TRADE

Suppliers of millinery materials (linings, wire, petershams, blocking nets) everything you need for the manufacture of hats. Blocking service available.

The Hat Trade. 3 Nevill Street, Tunbridge Wells, Kent TN2 5RZ
Tel/Fax: 01892 547847

HERALD & HEART HATTERS LTD

Millinery supplies.

Herald & Heart Hatters Ltd. 131 st. Phillip street, Battersea, London SW8 3SS
Tel: 020 7627 2414 Fax: 020 7652 2414

D. INNES, FROM THE NECK UP

Millinery supplies (straws, felts, petersham ribbon, veilings etc.) mail order only.
The British School of Millinery - Millinery classes.

D. Innes. From the Neck Up, 84 Hampden Road, Harrow HA3 5PR
Tel/Fax: 020 8427 7429

JAFFE

Manufacturers of loose feathers and feather trimmings, feather quill pens, feather brooches and replica feather butterflies.

Jaffe. The Old Brushworks, Castle Hill, Axminster, Devon EX13 5PY
Tel: 01297 33408 Fax: 01297 34574

THE DYER'S HAND

Hand dyed and painted cottons, silks, satins and velvets. Procion dyes, fabrics for dyeing, threads and fabrics hand dyed to order. Mail order/personal callers by appointment.

The Dyer's Hand. Sandra Wymann, 1 Welton Road, Leeds LS6 1EE
Tel/Fax: 0113 224 9877

EMBSAY MILLS

Patchwork and quilting fabrics, supplies and accessories.

Embsay Mills. Embsay, Skipton, North Yorkshire BD23 6QE
Tel: 01756 700946

FABERDASHERY

Patchwork fabrics available in packs. Monthly newsletter.

Faberdashery. Cockfield House, 48 Front Street, Cockfield, Bishop Auckland DL13 5DS
Tel: 01388 718838   Fax: 01388 710425

FASHION n' FABRICS

American cotton fabrics available in packs.

Fashion n' Fabrics. 24 Beech Road, St. Albans, Hertfordshire AL3 5AS
Tel: 01727 865038

GREEN HILL PATCHWORK & QUILTING

Patchwork and quilting shop selling American cottons, fabrics, books, threads and accessories. Mail order available.

Green Hill Patchwork & Quilting. 5 Tee Court, Bell Street, Romsey, Hampshire SO51 8GY
Tel: 01794 514826   Fax: 01794 511109

HEIRS & GRACES

Quilting and patchwork supplies and accessories, fabrics, books, etc.

Heirs & Graces. The Old Chapel, Buxton Road, Longnor, Nr. Buxton, SK17 0NY
Tel/Fax: 01298 83894

HIGGLEDY PIGGLEDY PATCHWORK SUPPLIES

American cotton fabrics, calico's, felts, waddings, threads, patterns, books and sundries. Debbie Mumms Friendship Host Shop. Mystery quilt and block of the month. Retail and mail order available.

**Higgledy Piggledy Patchwork Supplies. 26 Carr Field Drive, Luddenden,
Nr Halifax, West Yorkshire HX2 6RJ**
Tel/Fax: 01422 884431

HOUSE OF PATCHWORK

Patchwork and quilting fabrics, supplies and classes. Retail and mail order.

House of Patchwork. 52 Ware Road, Hoddesdon, Hertfordshire EN11 9DU
Tel: 01992 447544

INCA STUDIO

One stop shopping for students and specialists stocking unusual fabrics, patchwork materials, accessories, threads, ribbons, buttons and books.

Inca Studio. 10 Duke Street, Princes Risborough, Buckinghamshire HP27 OAT
Tel: 01844 343343 Fax: 01844 201263

LITTLE L'S FABRICS

American cotton fabrics, wadding, craft button packs, range of accessories.

Little L'Fabrics. 6 The Square, Dunchurch, Rugby, Warwickshire CV22 6NU
Tel: 01788 810959

MOORS SILK QUILTS

Print and plain fabrics.

Moors Silk Quilts. Paddons Row, Brook Street, Tavistock, Devon PL19 0HF
Tel: 01822 612624 Fax: 01822 611106.

PATCHWORK COTTAGE

Patchwork and quilting supplies. Mail order available.

Patchwork Cottage. Newton of Carmyllie by Arbroath DD11 2RA
Tel/Fax: 01241 860321

PATCHWORK HOUSE

Patchwork suppliers - retail and mail order.

Patchwork House. 2-3 Charlecombe Court, Stoke Lane, Westbury-on-Trym, Bristol BS9 3RL
Tel: 0117 9079991 Fax: 0117 9079992

PATCHWORKERS' PARADISE

Everything for the patchworker: rotary cutters, blades, boards, quilting accessories, fabrics, rulers and books etc. Retail and mail order.

Patchworkers' Paradise. 16 East Street, Blandford, Dorset DT11 7DR
Tel: 01258 456099

PATCHWORK PLUS

Patchwork fabrics, quilting materials, workstands, frames, lamps, embroidery threads, quilting accessories, millinery, haberdashery, notions and specialist books. Open every day. Mail order available.

Patchwork Plus. 129 Station Road, Cark, Grange-over-Sands, Cumbria LA11 7NY
Tel/Fax: 015395 559009

PATCHWORK & QUILTS

Fabrics, books, battings, stencils and general retail and mail order service.

Patchwork & Quilts. 9 West Place, Wimbledon Common, London SW19 4UH
Tel: 020 8946 1643

PHOENIX FIBRES

Polyester fibre fillings, polystyrene beads, polyester wadding.

Phoenix Fibres Ltd. Saffron Works, Saffron Lane, Leicester LE2 6UJ
Tel: 0116 283 4906 Fax: 0116 283 4616

PIECEMAKERS

Extensive range of fabrics - workshops for all levels.

Piecemakers. 13 Manor Green Road, Epsom, Surrey KT19 8RA
Tel: 01372 743161 Fax: 01372 748377

PIGLETS PATCH

Patchwork and quilting supplies, books, mats and cutters etc. Mail order available, callers by prior appointment.

Piglets Patch. 29 Gale Moor Avenue, Gosport, Hampshire PO12 2SG
Tel: 01705 345042

QUILT BASICS

Quilting accessories, tools, stencils, books, wadding, machine and hand quilting frames. Fabrics retail and mail order. Catalogue available - 3 x 1st class stamps.

Quilt Basics. Unit 19, Chiltern House, Waterside, Chesham, Buckinghamshire HP5 1PS
Tel: 01494 791401 Fax: 01442 827069

QUILT DIRECT LTD

Tools and accessories for quilting, sewing and pressing: pressing hams, rolls and boards, specialist threads, cutting mats, patchwork templates, stretching frames and haberdashery.

Quilt Direct Ltd. 11 Iliffe House, Iliffe Avenue, Oadby, Leicester LE2 5LS
Tel: 0116 271 0033 Fax: 0116 271 0099

THE QUILT FABRIC STUDIO

A wide selection of American cottons. Mail order service.

The Quilt Fabric Studio. 75 Queens Den, Aberdeen AB15 8BN
Tel: 01224 325333

THE QUILT LOFT

Run by quilters for quilters. American cotton fabrics, batiks and flannels. American books and magazines.

The Quilt Loft. 9-10 Havercraft Buildings, North Street, Worthing, West Sussex BN11 1DY
Tel: 01903 233771

THE QUILT ROOM

Patchwork and quilting retail and mail order specialists, fabrics, templates, rulers, specialist books. Day workshops, advice and guidance available. Mail order colour catalogue.

The Quilt Room. (Mail order), Rear Carvilles, Station Road, Dorking RH4 1XH
Tel: 01306 877307 Fax: 01306 740739
The Quilt Room. 20 West Street, Dorking, Surrey RH4 1BL
Tel: 01306 740739

RIO DESIGNS

Software available for quilters.

Rio Designs. Flint Cottage, Treacle Lane, Rushden, Buntingford, Hertfordshire SG9 0SL
Tel/Fax: 01763 288234

ROOFTOP FRAMES & FABRICS

Patchwork and quilting fabrics, quilting accessories, books, quilting magazines, machine embroidery, metallics and quilting threads.

Rooftop Frames & Fabrics. Jiggery Pokery, Mickley, Stocksfield, Northumberland NE43 7BG
Tel: 01661 844336

SEWING MACHINE CENTRE

Patchwork and quilting retail outlet. Mail order available. Over 200 - 100% American plains, over 1000 - 100% American prints, 100's of pre-printed panels and wide range of accessories and specialist books.

Sewing Machine Centre. 45, Crellin Street, Barrow-in-Furness, Cumbria LA14 1DS
Tel/Fax: 01229 823714

SEW & SO

Specialists in patchwork, quilting and embroidery supplies. Also offering courses and workshops. Mail order service - details available.

Sew & So. 16 Upper Olland Street, Bungay, Suffolk NR35 1BG
Tel: 01986 896147 Fax: 01986 896147

THE SKEP MILL SHOP

A huge range of craft cottons.

The Skep Mill Shop. Reuben Gaunts, Broom Mills, Coal Hill Lane, Farsley, Leeds
Tel: 0113 255 6769

STITCH N' TIME

Patchwork and quilting supplies, fabrics and accessories.

Stitch N' Time, 293 Sandycombe Road, Kew, Surrey TW9 3LU
Tel: 0181 948 8462

STRAWBERRY FAYRE FABRICS

Specialist patchwork and quilting suppliers. 100% Plain coloured and small print cotton fabrics - USA. 300 small design prints, textures etc. 200 plain cotton colours, natural unbleached cottons for dyeing, wadding, threads and notions. Send 10 first class stamps for sample pack and details.

Strawberry Fayre Fabrics. Chagford, Devon TQ13 8EN
Tel: 01647 433250

THREADBEAR SUPPLIES

Waddings and battings.

Threadbear Supplies. 11 Northway, Deanshanger, Milton Keynes MK19 6NF

BALLOU FINDINGS

A wide selection of findings available.

Ballou Trimmings. 15 Cochran Close, Crownhill, Milton Keynes MK8 0AJ
Tel: 01908 569311 Fax: 01908 260262

BARNETT & LAWSON TRIMMINGS LTD

A wonderful selection of trimmings: fur, metallic cords, braids, fringing, frogging, buttons, bobble fringing, fabric flowers, chenille trims, feathers boas and beads.

Barnett & Lawson Trimmings Ltd. 16-17 Little Portland Street, London W1N 6NE
Tel: 020 636 8591/4 Fax: 020 758 0669

BEAUTIFUL RIBBONS & CRAFTS

Stockists of ribbons. Beautiful Ribbons: satins, tartans, ginghams, wire edge, grossgrain, sheers, jacquards, spots, bows and roses.

Beautiful Ribbons & Crafts. 86 Boutport Street, Barnstaple, Devon EX31 1SR

F. BECK LTD

Manufacturers of braids, buttons, frogging. UK agents for Menoni, metal components.

F. Beck Ltd. 402 Harrow Road, London W9 2HU
Tel: 020 7286 9951 Fax: 020 7266 3391

BERISFORDS RIBBONS LTD

"The Ribbon People", ribbons, bindings, trimmings, bows, packaging and accessories.

Berisfords Ribbons Ltd. PO Box 2, Thomas Street, Congleton, Cheshire CW12 1EF
Tel: 01260 274011 Fax: 01260 274014

BRITISH TRIMMINGS

Manufacturers of decorative trimmings and accessories for home decoration, costume and fashion.

British Trimmings. PO Box 46, Coronation Street, Stockport, Cheshire SK5 7PJ
Tel: 0800 214455 Fax: 0800 213344

BRITISH TRIMMINGS

Manufacturers of decorative trimmings and accessories for home decoration, upholstery trimmings, soft furnishings and fashion articles. Mail order service where staff will match fabrics sent with various products for customers who are unable to visit the retail outlet. Discounted furnishing trimmings and accessories.

British Trimmings. Ball Haye Road, Leek, Staffordshire ST13 6AU
Tel: 01538 383634 Fax: 01538 399024

CASCADE

Mail order trimmings, decorative braids, scrolls and fringes.

Cascade. 41 Queens Avenue, Barnsley S75 2AZ

THE CLASSIC DESIGN

Decorative ribbons and trimmings.

The Classic Design. PO Box 248, Shoreham-by-Sea, BN43 5SQ
Tel/Fax: 01273 452311

C. L. TRADING COMPANY

Exclusive range of handbeaded motifs and trims available. Bridal sequin and beaded rhinestones, lace, satin, braided velvet, cord, fasteners, trims, velvet and fur trims.

C. L. Trading Company. 140 Northgate, Newark, Nottinghamshire NG24 1HJ
Tel/Fax: 01636 674422

CMP HABICO LTD

Wholesalers of haberdashery, trimmings and craft products: motifs, lurex trims, lace, insertion piping, fringing, feathers, fasteners, bridal lace, binding, beads etc.

CMP Habico Ltd. Units B4-5, Wellington Road Industrial Estate, Leeds LS12 2UA
Tel: 0113 244 9810   Fax: 0113 242 5077

CRAFT CREATIONS LTD

Ribbons, rosebuds and bows.

Craft Creations. 2A Ingersol House, Delamere Road, Chestnut, Hertfordshire EN8 9ND
Tel: 01992 781903

CRAFTY RIBBONS

Ribbon designs: Wire edge, Thai, designer prints, sheer, metallic, velvets, American designs etc.

Crafty Ribbons. 3 Beechwood, Clump Farm, Tin Pot Lane, Blandford, Dorset DT11 7TS
Tel: 01258 455889 Fax: 01258 456060

DIXIE COLLECTIONS

Silk ribbons, miniature trims, lace, haberdashery and craft supplies.
Mail order catalogue available £2.60 plus SAE.

Dixie Collections. 4 Coney Hall Parade, Kingsway, Coney Hall, West Wickham, Kent BR4 9JB
Tel: 020 8462 0700

EATON'S SEASHELLS

Miniature and small shells.

Eaton's Seashells. 30 Forest Drive West, London E11 1LA
Tel/Fax: 020 8539 5288

THE FINISHING TOUCH

Manufacturers and retailers of top quality sew on appliqué and diamante heat transfers. Small range of crystal buttons also available.

The Finishing Touch. The Corner House, Norton Street, Grantham, Lincolnshire NG31 6BY
Tel/Fax: 01476 593400

FLOWERS BY NOVELTY

Manufacturer and importers of artificial flowers for dresses, accessories, shoes, hats etc. Mail order catalogue available.

Flowers By Novelty. Unit 1. Mill Lane, Fullbridge, Maldon, Essex CM9 4NX
Tel: 01621 854981 Fax: 01621 858761

GLITTERATI

A wide range of trimmings available.

Glitterati. 215 Chapel House, 24 Nutford Place, Marble ARCH, London W1H 6AE
Tel: 020 7723 2255 Fax: 020 7224 8722

GOODYEAR & UHLMAN

Trimmings, lace inserts, buttons, strings of pearls and sequins, beads, embroidery, threads etc.

Goodyear & Uhlman. Pimbo, Samros House, 1A Finsbury Park Road, London N4 2LA
Tel/Fax: 01282 450914

HAMILWORTH FLORAL PRODUCTS

Japanese flower ribbons.

Hamilworth Floral Products. 23 Lime Road, Dumbarton, Dumbartonshire.

JAFFE

Manufacturers of loose feathers and feather trimmings for fashion, costume, millinery and display. Trade only.

Jaffe. The Old Brushworks, Castle Hill, Axminster, Devon EX13 5PY
Tel: 01297 33408 Fax: 01297 34574

JOMIL

Wholesale haberdashery, furnishing, trims and craft supplies.

Jomil. 1007 Great Horton Road, Bradford BD7 4AH
Tel: 01274 578997 Fax: 01274 576303 & 770266

KALA EMPORIUM LTD

Exporters, importers and manufacturers of a wide range of trimmings, braids, sequins, tassels, fringes, rhinestones, mirrors, motifs, specialising in beaded fringing from 3" to 18" used in line dancing. Costume jewellery, trimmings, braids and beads.

Kala Emporium Ltd. 134 Station Street West, Coventry CV6 5ND
Tel: 01203 686457 & 682404 Fax: 01203 637057

KARADIA TRIMS LTD

Crochet trims, fringes, knitted trims, braids, eyelets, overlocking threads, zips, bows etc.

Karadia Trims Ltd. Eastern Boulevard, Rydel Street, Leicester LE2 7BF
Tel: 0116 233 3434 Fax: 0116 233 3608

KLEINS

Stocks everything from the practical to the fantastical: sequins, trims, braids, tassels, fluffy boas, fastenings, buckles, webbing, boning, underwires and bra adjustments.

Kleins. 5 Noel Street, London W1V 3RB
Tel: 020 7437 6162   Fax: 020 7437 1571

KWACHA LTD

Specialists in garment trimmings and packaging: zips, buttons, cords, piping, sewing cottons, yarns, elastics and packaging: boxes, bags etc.

Kwacha Ltd. 124-126 Weymouth Street, Leicester LE4 6FQ
Tel: 0116 266 0662 Fax: 0116 261 0772

LEICESTER THREAD & TRIMMING MANUFACTURERS LTD

Wide variety of trimmings, fringings, edgings, motifs, threads etc.

Leicester Thread & Trimming Manufacturers Ltd. 107 Barkby Road, Leicester LE4 9LG
Tel: 0116 276 5858
Also at:
Dean Street Mills, Dean Street, Derby DE22 3PU
Tel: 01332 345250 Fax: 01332 344851

MAC CULLOCH & WALLIS (LONDON) LTD

Mail order, wholesale and retail. Fabrics, trims, millinery supplies, embroidery threads, ribbons, braids, linings and interlinings, silk, bridal and tailoring.

Mac Culloch & Wallis (London) Ltd. 25-26 Dering Street, London W1R 0BH
Tel: 020 7629 0311 Fax: 020 7491 9578

V. M. MASON & CO LTD

Fixed or swivel jeans buttons, single or twin prong, press fasteners and zips

V.M.Mason & Co Ltd. 49 Lawrence Road, London NI5 4EG
Tel: 0181 802 4227/8 Fax: 0181 809 6291

MEDWAY FEATHER COMPANY

Wholesale feather merchant.

Brasenose Road, Gillingham, Medway, Kent ME7 4JR
Tel: 01634 852841 Fax: 01634 280318

MIDLAND TRIMMINGS

Wholesale suppliers of all haberdashery and trimmings: embroidery kits, motifs, threads, stiffenings, laces, bridal flowers and accessories, craft accessories. Mail order service available and trade cash and carry.

Midland Trimmings. Egypt Road, New Basford Industrial Estate, Baseford, Nottingham NG7 7GD
Tel: 0115 970 1802 Fax: 0115 970 2648

M. J. J. TRIMCRAFT HOUSE

Educational suppliers of craft and haberdashery items. Collage, ribbons, braids, ribbons, beads, lace, sequins, velcro, feathers, tapestry and embroidery materials.

M. J. J. Trimcraft House. 100 Springhall Lane, Halifax HX1 4TW
Tel: 01422 381 723 Fax: 01422 381725

MIRRORS

Octagonal, rectangal, square and oval shaped mirrors in different sizes.

Mirrors. Tel: 01908 612236

J. T. MORGAN - HABERDASHER

Button, braids, buttons, ribbons and trimmings.

J. T. Morgan. Shop 28, Chepstow Corner, Chepstow Place, London W2
Tel: 020 7229 1011

NOSTALGIA

Ribbon specialists for embroidery and ribbon work, French wire edge, bias hand dyed silk, velvet organdy, georgette, rayon beaded, silk printed and embroidery embellishments.

Nostalgia. 147A Nottingham Road, Eastwood, Nottingham NG16 3GJ
Tel: 01773 712240

NOTTINGHAM LACES & TRIMMINGS

Laces, trimmings and fabrics especially for bridalwear. Wholesale and retail. Mail order catalogue and samples available. Showroom at Long Eaton.

Nottingham Laces & Trimmings. Turret E, Harrington Mills, Leopald Street, Long Eaton, Nottingham NG10 8QE
Tel: 0115 946 0766 Fax: 0115 946 0741

NOVA TRIMMINGS LTD

Wholesale suppliers of a wide range of all fabrics and trimmings for all types of trades: threads, zips, lace, labels, buttons, printed and plain fabrics.

Nova Trimmings Ltd. Unit 2, Abbeygate House, 15 Abbeygate, Leicester LE4 0AA
Tel: 0116 253 1144 Fax: 0116 251 5631

C. M. OFFRAY & SON EUROPE

Decorative ribbons in widths from 1.5mm to 70mm. Washable, as well as wired decorative designs. Prints, jacquards and plain weaves such as satins, grosgrains, sheers, and a large collection of roses and bows.

C. M. Offray & Son Europe. Roscrea, Co. Tipperary, Ireland
Tel: INT + 353 505 21811 Fax: INT + 353 505 22392

OSTRICH FEATHER MANUFACTURING COMPANY LTD

Manufacturers of feathers and trimmings for dresswear, hats, boleros, capes and stoles etc. Maribou yardage, cock feathers, ostrich trimming and maribou boleros.

Ostrich Feather Manufacturing Company Ltd. 11 North Burgh Street, London EC1V 0AH
Tel: 020 7253 4140/7391

PINTAIL PRODUCTS

Feather specialists.

Pintail Products. Langrick Road, Hubberts Bridge, Lincolnshire PE20 3SG
Tel: 01205 290448

POINT NORTH

Mail order company selling fabrics and accessories for all outdoor pursuits. Trimmings, buckles, fasteners, toggles, cords, chain and heavy duty zips, zip pullers, wadding, shock cord, hooks etc.

Point North. Porthdafarch Road, Holyhead, Anglesey LL65 2LP

RANDALL & CO. (RIBBONS)

Ribbons, artificial flowers, feathers and trimmings, veilings, organza, satins, cotton polyesters, hat pins and millinery wire.

Randall & Co. (Ribbons). 12 Frederick Street, Luton LU2 7QS
Tel: 01582 721301

RIBBON DESIGNS

Mail order specialising in pure silk, organdy and narrow satin ribbons for embroidery, patchwork, appliqué, weaving and a host of exciting ideas to fire the imagination.

Ribbon Designs. PO Box 382, Edgware, Middlesex HA8 7XQ
Tel/Fax: 020 8958 4966

THE RIBBON REEL

Sheer ribbons in over 20 shades.

The Ribbon Reel. 157 Southborough Lane, Bickley, Kent BR2 8AP
Tel: 020 8467 9081

V. V. ROULEAUX

Trimmings galore, ribbons, wired organza, tassels, woven braids etc.

V. V. Rouleaux. 10 Symons Street, London SW3

SELECTUS LTD

Manufacturers of Panda® ribbons and narrow fabrics including satins, taffetas, failles, velvets, woven and printed fancies, tartans, metallics, Rigilene® boning, petershams and bias binding.

Selectus Ltd. The Uplands, Biddulph, Stoke on Trent, ST8 7RH
Tel: 01782 511288

SILVAN LTD

Lace trimmings, gold and silver lace available.

Silvan Ltd. 21 Blandford Street, London W1H 3AD

H. SUSKIN (TEXTILES) LTD

Haberdashery and trimmings for the textile trade, very large ranges.
Cash and carry and mail order - export welcomed.

H. Suskin (Textiles) Ltd. Harley House, Wharf Road, Stratford, London E15 2SU
Tel: 0208 534 8800 Fax: 0208 519 4582

SWAROVSKI UK LTD

Specialists in rhinestone, pearlised, metallic and reflective elements incorporated into trimmings, transfers, zips, buttons and components. A wide range of designs available and special transfer designs made to customers requirements and specifications.

Swarovski UK Ltd. Perrywood Business Park, Honey Crock Lane, Salfords, Surrey RH1 5JQ
Tel/Fax: 01737 856800

TEMPTATION ALLEY

Trimmings, tassels, fringing, ribbons, maribou, fake feathers etc. A whole range of inexpensive fabrics.

Temptation Alley. 361 Portobello Road, London W10 5SA
Tel: 020 8964 2004

TEXTILE EXPRESSION

Fabrics for contemporary design, dyes and colouring media, handmade papers, decorative threads and embroidery ribbons.

Textile Expression. 31 Belmont Road, Burton-upon-Trent, Staffordshire DE13 9NL
Tel: 01283 520496 Fax: 01283 520878

TOPAZ TRIMS (UK) LTD

Trimming specialists, bridal collection includes beaded, laces, guipures, corded laces, edgings, motifs, and fabrics. Fashion trims, appliques, Iron-on, feather boas, fringes, tassels, froggings, beaded buttons and trims. Mail order - £100 - carriage paid.

Topaz Trims (UK) Ltd. Topaz House, 465 Hornsey Road, London N19 4DR
Tel: 020 7609 1000 Fax: 020 7281 7408

THE TRIMMINGS COMPANY

Supplier of fashion trimmings: feathers, lace, beading, elastics, laces and many more to the manufacture trade.

The Trimmings Company. 5 Harp Business Centre, Aspley Way, London NW2 7LR
Tel: 020 8208 4200 Fax: 020 8452 0056

WALTONS MILL SHOP

A wide range of braids, cords and trimmings.

Walton Mill Shop. 41 Tower Street, Harrogate HG1 1HS
Tel: 01423 520980

W. M. BEDI LTD

Wholesalers of lace and trimmings, edgings, lace, broderie anglais, braids, ribbons, bridal trimmings etc.

W. M. Bedi Ltd. 27 St Mary's Gate, Nottingham NG1 1PJ
Tel: 0115 9505572 Fax: 0115 9411669

ABBEY QUILTING LTD

Natural kapok, lambswool and polyester wadding.

Abbey Quilting Ltd. Selinas Lane, Dagenham, Essex RM18 1ES
Tel: 020 8592 2233 Fax: 020 8593 3787

A. E. ARTHUR LTD

Ardis dress forms.

A. E. Arthur Ltd. Ardis House, Rollesby Road, Hardwick Industrial Estate, Kings Lynn, Norfolk PE30 4LS
Tel: 01553 763252

BUTTERICK COMPANY LTD

Distributors of Vogue, Butterick, See & Sew paper patterns, an extensive selection of sewing related books, magazines and videos. Educational resource packs and cross stitch kits also available.

Butterick Company Ltd. New Lane, Havant, Hampshire PO9 2ND
Tel: 01705 486221 Fax: 01705 492769

COATS CRAFTS UK

Manufacturers and distributors of needlecraft, handknitting, sewing and haberdashery to the retail trade. Core brands include: Anchor, Drima, Sylko, Patons and Millards.

Coats Crafts UK. PO Box 22, The Lingfield Estate, Mc Mullen Road, Co. Durham DL1 1YQ
Consumer Helpline: 01325 365457

CMP HAMBICO LTD

Haberdashery and trimmings, craft products, lace, bindings, beads etc.

CMP Hambico Ltd. Units B4-5, Wellington Road Industrial Estate, Leeds LS12 2UA
Tel: 0113 244 9810 Fax: 0113 242 5077

CREATIVE GRIDS

Cutting equipment, mats and cut and press boards, rulers, wadded and gridded vilene.

Creative Grids. PO Box 207, Leicester LE3 6YP
Tel/Fax: 0116 2857151

H. CUBITT BEXFIELD LTD

Specialist suppliers of scissors and shears, also supplying haberdashery and craft products.

H. Cubitt Bexfield Ltd. Mundial House, Kiveton Park Station, Kiveton Park, Sheffield S26 6NP
Tel: 01909 772866 Fax: 01909 773410

DRESSMAKERS WHOLESALE

Wholesale supplier of fabrics and haberdashery: zips, buttons, beads, fastenings, sewing and embroidery threads, dyes etc. Mail order and cash and carry.

Dressmakers Wholesale. Unit 41, Faraday Mill, Faraday Park, Prince Rock, Plymouth PL4 0ST
Tel/Fax: 01752 255662 Tel: 0589 714080

EASTMAN MACHINE COMPANY LTD

Scissors, shears, spot and cross paper, patternmasters, pattern notchers, economy pattern paper, general fashion equipment and books for the apparel industry.

Eastman Machine Company Ltd. Duro House, Station Estate, Eastwood Close, London E18 1BY
Tel: 020 8989 7784

EMPRESS MILLS (1927) LTD

Sewing thread manufacturer. A wide range of threads for all types of machine and hand sewing, industrial, wholesale and retail. Mill prices. Free mail order fact pack. Ring: 01282 863181

Empress Mills (1927) Ltd. Hollin Hall Mill, Trawden, Colne, Lancashire BB8 8SS
Tel: 01282 863181 Fax: 01282 870935

THE FORGE MILL NEEDLE MUSEUM

An extensive range of hand and machine needles available from the museum shop or by mail order.

The Forge Mill Needle Museum. Needle Mill Lane, Riverside, Redditch, Worcestershire BA8 8HY
Tel: 01527 62508

FREUDENBERG NONWOVENS LTD

Fusable interfacings - vilene, iron on edge tape, high bulk volume fleece, shoulder pads etc.

Freudenberg Nonwovens Ltd. Vilene retail, PO Box 3, Greetland, Halifax, West Yorkshire HX4 8NJ
Tel: 01422 313000 Fax: 01422 313142

HARLEQUIN

Mail order manufacturer of covered buttons, belts and many other accessories available made from your own fabric or from our own range.

Harlequin. Riverside Avenue, West Manningtree, Essex C01 1UX
Tel: 01206 396167 Fax: 01206 397008

HUSQVARNA VIKING

Swedish sewing machine manufacturer of embroidery, computerised and electronic domestic machines. Also supplier of embroidery software packages and sewing machine accessories.

Husqvarna Viking. Viking House, Cheddar Business Park, Wedmore Road, Cheddar, Somerset BS27 3EB
Tel: 01934 744533 Fax: 01934 744811

HEART OF ENGLAND SEWING MACHINES

Supply, service and training in the use of computer sewing machines to schools and business. Mail order textile supplies and haberdashery. Multi-cultural supplies for schools and colleges.

Heart of England Sewing Machines. 9 Alverston Grove, Knowle, Solihull, West Midlands B93 9NT
Tel: 01564 772156 Fax: 01564 777801

INTERNATIONAL SHOULDERPAD COMPANY LTD

ISC are the specialist suppliers in shoulder pads to the garment and manufacturing industry. Manufacturing tailored and fibre shoulderpads, bra cups and sleeve heads.

International Shoulder Pads. Unit 2, Swinnow Court, 617 Staningley Road, Leeds, West Yorkshire LS13 4ER
Tel: 0113 236 3150 Fax: 0113 236 3151

JMM MARKETING

Haberdashery.

J M M Marketing. Oaktree View House, The Crossway, Churt, Farnham GU10 2JE
Tel: 01428 717357 Fax: 01428 712242

JOHN DUFFY SEWING THREADS

Wholesale thread merchant. Sensational sewing threads prices - quality products at unbeatable prices. Mail order speciality, send no money.

John Duffy. 457 Christchurch Road, Boscombe, Bournemouth, Dorset BH1 4AD
Tel: 01202 300080 Fax: 01202 469240

JUST NEEDLES

Large range of needles in stock, from beading needles to gloving needles.
Just Needles. Freephone: 0808 100 1541

KENNETT & LINSELL LTD

Kennett & Linsell Ltd. design and manufacture tailors dummies for the clothing industry and for education. Pattern cutting and grading equipment also available.

Kennett & Linsell Ltd. Crow Lane, Romford, Essex RM7 0ES
Tel: 01708 749732 Fax: 01708 733328

KINROSS (SUPPLIES)

Stockists of polycotton and polyester industrial sewing threads for overlocking and lockstitch machines, supplying to the home dressmaker and small units - mail order.

Kinross (Supplies). PO Box 55, Pinner HA5 4UL
Tel: 020 8421 1685

LAKELAND LTD

Yarn, sewing organiser - hobby boxes.

Lakeland Ltd. Alexandra Buildings, Windermere, Cumbria LA23 1BQ
Tel: 01539 488100 Fax: 01539 488300

MORPLAN

Mail order company supplying over 6000 products for the fashion industry. Clothing and manufacture equipment, retail products etc.

Morplan. PO Box 54, Harlow, Essex CM20 2TS
Tel: 0800 435 333 Fax: 0800 451928

NEEDLE NEEDS

Portable magnifyer, light stands, floor frames and needlecraft stands.

Needleneeds. The Old Bakery, 9 St Mary Street, Nether Stowes, Bridgwater, Somerset TA5 1LJ
Tel/Fax: 01278 733633

NEWEY TEXTILES (UK) LTD

Sewing accessories: boning, fasteners, hooks and eyes and tapes. Manufacturers of components for bra's including hook and eye tape, nylon coated metal rings, slides and ultrasonic - sealed shoulder straps etc.

Newey Textiles (UK) Ltd. Sedgley Road, West Tipton, West Midlands DY4 8AH
Tel: 0121 522 2500 Fax: 0121 522 6357

PERIVALE - GÜTERMANN LTD

Manufacturers and distributors of retail and industrial sewing threads, YKK retail zips, suppliers of the new range of Gütermann 'Creativ' beads and sequins.

Perivale - Gütermann Ltd. Wadsworth Road, Greenford, Middlesex UB6 7JS
Tel: 020 8998 5000 Fax: 020 8810 4821

PHOENIX FIBRES

Polyester fibre filling, polystyrene beads, polyester wadding.

Phoenix Fibres. Saffron Works, Saffron Lane, Leicester LE2 6UJ
Tel: 0116 283 4906 Fax: 0116 283 4616

PROSHARP

Sharpening and tailors shears. All inclusive sharpening and replacement of scissors, knives and woodworking and craft tooling. All trades and professions use PROSHARP. Postal sharpening service.

Prosharp. 29 Prospect Place, Hayle, Cornwall TR27 4LU Tel/Fax: 01736 756162

QUILT DIRECT LTD

Pressing hams, rolls and boards, specialist threads, cutting mats and rotary cutters, stretching frames and a wide range of haberdashery.

Quilt Direct Ltd. 11 Iliffe House, Illife Avenue, Oadby, Leicester LE2 5LS
Tel: 0116 271 0033 Fax: 0116 271 0099

R. L. & C. M. BOND

Haberdashery.

R. L. & C. M. Bond. 93 Town Street, Farsley, West Yorkshire LS28 5HX
Tel: 0113 257 4905

SEWABILITY

Mail order sewing patterns: Sew Simple, Kwik-Sew, Stretch and Sew, Sewgrand.

Sewability. 22 Fassett Square, Hackney, London E8 1DQ
Tel: 020 7683 0253

SEWMASTER SEWING MACHINES

Main agents : Bernina, Pfaff, Husqvarna and Brother. Sales, service and spares.
Sewmaster Sewing Machines. 3 West Street, Reading, Berkshire RG1 1TT
Tel: 0118 957 1845 Fax: 0118 957 1603.
Also at 12 Epsom Road, Guildford
Tel: 01483 567609

SEW QUICK

Sewing accessories from America. Sewing machine feet, serger feet, instructional videos, books, sewing needles etc.
Sew Quick. 17 Calside, Paisley, Renfrewshire, Scotland PA2 6DA
Tel: 0141 889 7333

THE SEWING ROOMS LTD

Husqvarna, Viking sewing machines, haberdashery and sewing courses.
The Sewing Rooms Ltd. 14 Lacy Road, Putney, London SW15 1NL

SEWING WORLD

Sewing machines and overlockers, sales, service care. A wide range of haberdashery, dressmaking, crafts patterns, paper patterns - mail order available.
Sewing World. 308-310 Wimbourne Road, Winton Banks, Bournemouth, Dorset BH9 2HN
Tel: 01202 528451 Fax: 01202 775590

STAPLES GROUP PLC

Manufacture paper, spot and cross, haberdashery, trimmings, hooks and eyes, shoulder pads, interfacings/fusables, velcro, waistbands, garment bags and hangers etc.
Staples Group Plc. Lockwood Road, Huddersfield, West Yorkshire HD1 3QW
Tel: 01484 888 8888

SUPERMEND LTD

Repairs, rips, tears and cigarette burns in most fabrics invisibly. Use for many crafts, cardboard, paper and wood etc. for further information call now: public, trade or wholesale orders welcome.
Supermend Ltd. (Dept F), PO Box 300, Basildon, Essex SS14 3RT
Tel/Fax: 01268 271244

H. SUSKINS (TEXTILES) LTD

Haberdashery and trimmings for textile trades. Cash and carry, mail order and export welcomed.
H. Suskins (Textiles) Ltd. Harley House, Wharf Road, Stratford, London E15 2SU
Tel: 0208 534 8800 Fax: 0208 519 4582

UK SEWING SERVICES

Stockists and suppliers of quality sewing threads, elastics, cords, trimmings and press fasteners. Button covering machinery specialists.
UK Sewing Services. 88 Rocky Lane, Moston, Manchester M30 9LY
Tel: 0161 789 3898 Fax: 01978 357991

VILENE INTERLININGS

Manufacturers of non woven interfacings and sewing aids.

Vilene Interlinings. Lowfields Business Park, Ellend, West Yorkshire HX5 5DX
Tel: 01422 327900 Fax: 01422 327999

VINCE WHITE WHOLESALE

Distributors to the retail industry. Bindings, zips, traced goods lace trimmings, velcro and vilenes, felts, dylon dyes etc.

Vince White Wholesale. 47 Duckpool Road, Newport, Gwent NP9 8FL
Tel: 01633 257711/257733 Fax: 01633 214422

WILKINSON SCISSORS

Shears and scissors.

Wilkinson Scissors. 87 Studfield Hill, Sheffield S1 4SH
Tel: 0122 6718393

W. WILLIAMS & SON (BREAD STREET) LTD

Haberdashery and handicrafts: ribbons, beads, zips, threads and stencils.

W. William & Son (Bread Street) Ltd. Regent House, 1 Thane Villas, London N7 7PH
Tel: 020 7263 7311 Fax: 020 7281 0345

YKK FASTENERS

Pex zips, hooks and loop fasteners. All ranges, colours and sizes.

YKK Zips. 67 Derby Street, Manchester M8 8HE
Tel: 0161 832 3262 Fax: 0161 834 4704

ADELAIDE WALKER

Large range of quality fibres for handspinning, feltmaking and weaving, carders and creative embroidery packs available. Mail order.

Adelaide Walker. 2 Mill Yard Workshops, Otley Mills, Ilkley Road, Otley LS21 3JP
Tel/Fax: 01943 850812

ANNA CRUTCHLEY - PASSEMENTERIE

The Anna Crutchley's Cordtwister for spinning fine cords and chunky ropes, tassel moulds, jute yarn and the Tassel Book by Anna Crutchley are all available.
For a copy of the catalogue please send a SAE.

Anna Crutchley - Passementerie. The Frater Studio, 6B Priory Road, Cambridge CB5 8HT
Tel: 01223 327685

ASHILL COLOUR STUDIO

Mail order business supplying natural dyes, books, seeds and mordants.

Ashill Colour Studio. Boundary Cottage, 172 Clifton Road, Shefford, Bedfordshire SG17 5AH
Tel: 01462 812001

AVL LOOMS GB

The UK based agents for AVL Looms, USA's varied range of weaving looms.

AVL LOOMS GB. 40 Tarrant Street, Arundel, West Sussex BN18 9DN
Tel: 01903 884433 Fax: 01903 785323

BOZEDOWN ALPACAS

Alpaca breeder supplying exclusive luxury pure Alpaca and Alpaca/silk fabrics. Mail order available.

Bozedown Alpacas. Joy Whitehead, Lower Hitch, Whitechurch Hill,
Reading, Berkshire RG8 7NU
Tel: 0118 984 3827 Fax: 0118 984 3737

THE BYRE

Mail order hand spinning and weaving supplies.

The Byre. West Mains Granary, Blyth Bridge, West Linton, Peeblesshire EH46 7AH
Tel/Fax: 01721 752689

DAVID G. BARNETT

Maker of the Barnett Drum carding machine, first choice of spinners and felters. Mail order.

David G. Barnett. 4 St Peters Road, Seaford, East Sussex BN25 2HS
Tel/Fax: 01323 893725

DOLGELLAU DESIGNS

Cords, tassels, braids and buttons. Locker needle hooking with fabric or fibre. Off loom weaving. Lucet for making braids and wooden moulds for tassel making.
Textile artist and exhibitor.

Dolgellau Designs. Refail, Tir Stent Bach, Dolgellau, Gwynedd LL40 2RE
Tel: 01341 422790

DON PORRITT LOOMS / STUDIO SUPPLIES

Suppliers of the Toika and Louét Looms - Texsolv system and Heddles, stainless steel reeds, stretchers, shuttles, bobbin winders, reeds/threading hooks and warping equipment. Mail order suppliers.

Don Porritt Looms/Studio Supplies. The Studio, Leathley Road, Menston, Ilkley, West Yorkshire LS29 6DP
Tel: 01943 878329 Fax: 01943 878329

FARNHAM LOOM COMPANY

Distributors of Glimakra Swedish looms and accessories. Spare parts made for looms.

Farnham Loom Company. Hut Cottage, West Meon, Petersfield, Hampshire GU32 1JY
Tel/Fax: 01730 829452

FIBRECRAFTS

Textile books, videos and magazines on the textile arts. Spinning wheels, weaving looms, equipment and accessories. Dyestuffs supplies and chemicals for dyeing and batik, fibres and yarns. International mail order supplier.

Fibrecrafts. 1 Old Portsmouth Road, Peasmarsh, Guildford, Surrey GU3 1LZ
Tel: 01483 421853 Fax: 01483 419960 e-mail: Fybrecraft@aol.com

FRANK HERRING & SONS

A wide range of weaving looms (hand, table and floor), equipment, materials and books for spinners, weavers, dyers, feltmakers and lacemakers.

Frank Herring & Sons. 27 High West Street, Dorchester, Dorset DT1 1UP
Tel: 01305 264449 Fax: 01305 250675

FREDA ROBINSON - ARABESQUE BRAIDS

Plastic lucet - producing square knitted cord £3 inclusive p&p. Plastic disc produces Kumihimo style braid, also weaving, needle weaving and openwork. £4 inclusive p&p. Catalogue available SAE.

Freda Robinson - Arabesque Braids. 103 Wandsworth Road, Knock, Belfast BT14 3LU
Tel: 01232 655141

HELEN RIPPIN (WARATAH FIBRES)

Gaywool Dyes from Australia suitable for wool, silk and mohair. Helen Rippin also specialises in hand painted and hand dyed fibres. Workshops demonstrations and mail order.

Helen Rippin (Waratah Fibres). 3 Kirkham Street, Rodley, LS13 1JP
Tel/Fax: 0113 2557198

H. GROOM

Sheep fleeces for spinning & weaving. Various breeds include Masham, Merino, Jacob, Dorset, Teeswater and crosses producing coloureds etc. Large SAE for samples please. Mail order available.

H. Groom. Manor Farm, Dethick, Matlock, Derbyshire DE4 5GG
Tel: 01629 534246

HALDANES CRAFT & TOOLS LTD

Suppliers of Ashford spinning wheels, looms and accessories.

Haldanes Craft & Tools Ltd. Gateside, Strathmiglo, Fife KY14 7ST
Tel: 01337 860767 Fax: 01337 868983

THE HANDWEAVERS STUDIO & GALLERY LTD

Spinning and weaving supplies and tuition. A wide range of fibres, fleece, yarns and equipment, books and dyes. Mail order and personal callers welcome.

The Handweavers Studio & Gallery Ltd. 29 Haldstone Road, London E17 7AW
Tel: 020 8521 2281

HEDGEHOG EQUIPMENT

Mail order suppliers and makers of the Hedgehog Drum Carder, hand carders for wool spinners and felt making. Agents for spinning and weaving equipment.

Hedgehog Equipment. Meondene, Broadway Road, Mickleton, Gloucestershire GL55 6PT
Tel: 01386 438349

HILLTOP SPINNING & WEAVING CENTRE

Home of Easy Peasy Dyes, natural, acid, reactive, silk dyes and specialists in spinning and weaving supplies by mail order. Group and individual tuition. Free mail order brochure available on request. Textile craft courses available.

Hilltop Spinning and Weaving Centre. Windmill Cross, Canterbury Road, Lyminge Nr Folkstone, Kent CT18 8HD
Tel: 01303 862617

HIRAETH SILKS

Quality carded Shetland fleece, various colours from Trevan Flock, silk tops and natural dyed silk threads.

Hiraeth Silks. Anne Crossman, Cwn Cufn Ganal, Felinfach, Lampeter, Dyfed SA48 8PJ

KEMTEX SERVICES LTD
KEMTEX COLOURS

Suppliers of small quantities of chemical textile dyes (50 gms - 5 kilos), including: Procion, acid, direct, disperse and indigo plus a wide range of associated chemicals. Send SAE for details.

Kemtex Services Ltd. Kemtex Colours. Chorley Business & Technology Centre, Euxton Lane, Chorley, Lancashire PR7 6TE
Tel: 01257 230220 Fax: 01257 230225

LEANDA

Manufacturers of textile craft equipment, supplying mail order to spinners, weavers, embroiderers, textile artists and craft people worldwide. Specialists in Japanese braiding and tassel making.

Leanda. Scotts Yard, Ber Street, Norwich NR1 3HA
Tel: 01603 763340 Fax: 01603 765314

LITTLE LONDON SPINNERS

All requirements for spinning.

Little London Spinners. Unit 8, Home Farm, Rural Industries, East Tytherley Road, Lockerley, Romsey, Hampshire S05 0JT

THE LOOM EXCHANGE

Spinning and weaving equipment bought and sold. Catalogue available, please send large SAE.

The Loom Exchange. Ash House, Ash Stedham, Midhurst, Sussex, GU29 0PT
Tel/Fax: 01730 817191

LYN JENKINS

Spinning and weaving supplies. Stockist and Agent for: Ashford, Haldanes and Louet. Exhibitor and designer. Felt commissions. Tuition available.

Lyn Jenkins. Unit 10, The Pearoom Centre for Contemporary Craft, Station Yard, Heckington, Sleaford, Lincolnshire
Tel: 01529 460765

MARY EVE - HANDSPINNER

Spinning equipment, natural or dyed fleece, variety of breeds, exotic fibres. Demonstrations/lectures on the History of Spinning.

Mary Eve - Handspinner. Carters, Station Road, Wickham, Bishops Witham, Essex CM8 3JB
Tel: 01621 891405 Or 01860 906335 Fax: 01621 893528

MICHELLE GREEN & LIN BUTLIN

Handspinning service for handknitters, crocheter - dog combings.

Michelle Green & Lin Butlin. The Old School, Singleton, West Sussex PO18 OEZ
Tel: 01234 811783

THE NATURAL FIBRE COMPANY LTD

Small contract spinning and yarn designs. Mail order yarns for knitwear designers. Naturally coloured and rare wools in blends with mohair and silk. Cashcora yarns.

The Natural Fibre Company Ltd. Unit 12, Llambed Enterprise Park, Lampeter, Ceredigion SA48 8LT
Tel/Fax: 01570 422956

ORRIN LOOMS

Makers of the Rutland Folding Table Loom 24" & 32".

Orrin Looms. Meadow View, Llandinam, Newton Powys SY17 5BG
Tel/Fax: 01686 688522

P & M WOOLCRAFT

Spinning wheels, weaving looms, accessories and books.

P & M Woolcraft. Pindon End Cottage, Pindon End, Hanslope, Milton Keynes MK19 7HN
Tel: 01908 510277 Fax: 01908 511706

ROSS SERVICES

Distributors of Mabel Ross publications. Mail order only.

Ross Services. Alastair Ross, Compton House, Furnace Lane, Finedone Sidings, Wellingborough, Northants NN9 5NY

RYEDALE TEXTILES CRAFTS

Handspun yarns, hand-dyed fibres for spinners, weavers, feltmakers, embroiderers and patchworkers. (Small scale natural and chemical dyeing for students). Mail order available.

Ryedale Textiles Crafts. The Old Rectory, Barton le Street, Malton, North Yorkshire YO17 6PL
Tel: 01653 628285

SMALLWARES LTD

Knit-weave needles.

Smallwares Ltd. 17 Galena Road, King Street, Hammersmith, London W6 0LN

SOMETHING SHEEPY

Dyes and dyeing kits supplied mail order to spinners, knitters, feltmakers and rag ruggers. Also rug making tools and backing fabrics. SAE for price list.

Something Sheepy. Tom's Barn, Dennington Road, Framlingham, Suffolk IP13 9JL
Tel: 01728 723114

THE SPINSTER'S ALMANACK & WOOLGATHERINGS

A quarterly journal and other budget publications for spinners, dyers and other textile enthusiasts with international readership.

The Spinster's Almanack. Willow House, 11 Frederick Avenue, Carlton, Nottingham NG4 1HP
Tel: 0115 9873135

STANSFIELDS OF ALMONDBURY

Wooden hand looms and accessories custom built in Huddersfield. Dobby mechanisms, shafts, back beams, industrial, educational and domestic handloom makers, established over 100 years ago.

Stansfields of Almondbury. 13 Westgate, Aldonbury, Huddersfield HD5 8XF
Tel/Fax: 01484 531967

SUE HILEY. SILKS FOR HANDSPINNERS

Pure silk wadding, fibre yarns, ribbons, specialist books and much more about silk. Mail order. Visit by appointment. Silk products for handspinners, handweavers, quilters, embroiderers, needle workers and silk devotees.

Sue Hiley. Silks for Handspinners. The Mill, Tregoyd Mill, Three Cocks, Brecon, Powys, Wales LD3 0SW
Tel/Fax: 01497 847421

SUSSEX MERINOS

Superfine English Merino wool

Sussex Merinos. Playsters Farm, Herstmonceux, East Sussex BN27 IPX

TIMBERTOPS SPINNING WHEELS

A family partnership making homecrafted wheels, traditional styles for craftworkers. Exported worldwide. Colour brochure available.

Timbertops Spinning Wheels. "Wheel Lodge" 159 Main Street, Ashfordby, Leicestershire LE14 3TS
Tel/Fax: 01664 812320

TYNSELL HANDSPINNING WHEELS

Wheels, handspinning equipment: combs and hackles, superb quality fibres, (Merino for felters), for spinning and felting etc. American magazines, wide ranging booklist available. Mail order.

Tynsell Handspinning Wheels. 53 Cross Green Road, Huddersfield HD5 9XX
Tel: 01484 534273 Fax: 01484 518328

UNDY YARNCRAFTS

Suppliers of yarns and accessories for machine knitting, weaving, spinning, dyeing, crochet etc. Representatives of the British Angora Producers Marketing Association and the Angora Association. Suppliers of Angora rabbit fibre and yarn grown, processed and spun in Britain. Mail order available.

Undy Yarncrafts. The Old Temperance Hall, West End, Magor, Monmouthshire NP6 3HT
Tel: 01633 881183 Fax: 01633 881028

VAL MARSHALL

Spinning wheels, equipment for sale, tuition. Mail order available.

Val Marshall. Brooklands Cross Lane, Low Bentham, Lancaster LA2 7HA

WEAVERY

Weave design software consultancy. Individual or group training.

Weavery. 24 Cliffe Terrace, Keighley, West Yorkshire BD21 5DP
Tel: 01535 213301 Fax: 01535 691078

WINGHAM WOOL WORK

Mail order fibres, fleeces, yarns and books for spinners, weavers, feltmakers and embroiderers etc. (Schools and colleges also supplied).

Wingham Wool Work. 70 Main Street, Wentworth, Rotherham, South Yorkshire S62 7TN
Tel: 01226 742926 Fax: 01226 741166

WOOLGATHERINGS

Woolgatherings is a range of cheap instructional booklets on all aspects of handspinning and natural dyeing. SAE for full list.

Woolgatherings. Willow House, 11 Frederick Avenue, Carlton, Nottingham NG4 1HP
Tel: 0115 987 3135

WOOLS, WHEELS & WEAVING

Equipment suppliers, locker hooks and canvas. American magazines.

Wools, Wheels & Weaving. Hop Garden, Skenfrith, Abergavenny, Gwent NP7 8UE

YARNS OF CREATION t/a BOBTAILS

Handspun yarns and knitwear commisions undertaken to spin knit fleece: dog, cat and other animal fibres from your own pet.

Yarns of Creation. 220 Seaside Road, Aldbrough, Nr Hull, East Yorkshire HU11 4RY
Tel: 01964 527801

YARN & SHUTTLE

Weaving accessories, spinning wheels and equipment, yarn samples available. Mail order only.

Yarn & Shuttle. Tulip Tree House, Bagshot Road, Worplesdon Hill, Woking, Surrey GU22 OQY
Tel: 01483 472176

THE ASSOCIATION OF GUILDS OF WEAVERS SPINNERS AND DRYERS

Registered Charity No. 289590

The aims of the Association are to encourage and maintain integrity and excellence of craftsmanship'; to encourage a sense of beauty of material, texture, colour and design; to foster these aims for individuals through the Certificate of Achievement; to promote opportunities for the exchange of information through lectures, library facilities, conferences and exhibitions both locally and nationally; to further co-operation between member-Guilds and societies with like aims.

There are over 100 affiliated Guilds throughout Great Britain, and also some overseas Guilds world-wide. Individual Guilds are responsible for the running of their own affairs and each has a programme of events and lectures. The Association organisers biennial Summer Schools, Conferences and Exhibitions held in different parts of the UK.

The association publishes a quarterly magazine: The Journal for Weavers Spinners and Dyers which offers articles and information covering all three disciplines.

For further information and addresses of local Guild secretaries
please contact the Hon. Secretary:
Anne Dixon, 2 Bower Mount Road, Maidstone, Kent ME16 8AU. Tel: 01622 678429

Remember to mention the
FASHION & TEXTILE INFORMATION DIRECTORY
When ordering your supplies

FATEC
FASHION
AND
TEXTILE
EDUCATIONAL
CONSULTANCY

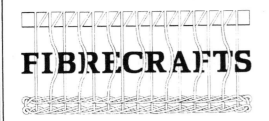

Leading Textile Arts Suppliers Merge

"Fabrics, colour and pattern design are the core of the new business. Designers, teachers, textile technicians and students are the customers to benefit from this merger."

George Weil was formed in 1895 as specialists in supplying silk and colour through dyes, paints and fabric printing inks.

Fibrecrafts is a leading supplier in Europe for products related hand made textile skills. In 18 years trading we have learned about natural fibres, yarns, dyes and inks to make and colour woven and felted fabrics.

Both are now working together to bring a unified service. The new 'One-Stop-Shop' is based in a new work place near Guildford. Fibrecrafts and George Weil offer an exciting range of products to meet the needs of textile art students and professionals.

The starting point for many textile artists is the fibre for spinning to yarn, or to make felt and paper fabrics. Fibres include the different breeds of British wools, each with their unique properties. Alongside are 18 colours of Merino, dyed to our own colour recipe for consistency over time. Fibrecrafts can supply many different fibres - from raw carded cocoon strippings to lustrous white silk sliver, line flax and cottons including natural green cotton sliver from the States.

The range of dyes and inks from George Weil, from Organics, through Acid, Direct and Procion MX dyes are all available. To these are added the assistants to modify and fix the colours to yarns for weaving, knitting or enhancing fabrics.

Then there are the yarns and looms to make woven cloth. The range of yarns is reviewed and developed from year to year as the team at Fibrecrafts seek new textures our customers will enjoy using. So Fibrecrafts can meet the needs of the rug weaver with a range of coloured thicker wools, apparel weight ecru yarns for dyeing for the cloth weaver to use, and more for the weaver wanting high twist fine yarn for a collapse cloth, through to paper yarns; both in colours from Sweden and naturals from England.

Once you have the fabric that is ready to be given your own unique touch, the range of products sold through Fibrecrafts and George Weil cannot help to excite and stimulate your creative talents. there are a full palette of fabric dyes, and paints as well as screen printing using water based and acrylic inks, and water based screen resists for the highest level safety.

George Weil and Fibercrafts lead in the range of products sold, because we constantly review and update our suppliers, always seeking the best products from around the world at the best price. This ranges from spinning wheel to a two-shaft table loom from New Zealand, a 32-shaft computerized loom from Holland, Swedish yarns, the latest American books and magazines or specialist spinning wheels, tapestry bobbins or dyes from the UK.

Fibrecrafts and George Weil strive to retain their leadership in the service we offer to you the customer. You can telephone, fax or e-mail your order to us. Orders received before 2.30 will normally be sent out the same day, you should receive your goods the next working day. All our customers appreciate this prompt service, and the professional assistance and advice that we are always willing to give.

To learn more about the service we can give you, see the Fibrecrafts and George Weil advertisements in this Directory.

THE AIRBRUSH AND SPRAY CENTRE LTD

Airbrush and compressor supplies, sales, service, spare parts and technical advice. Suppliers of paints and general art materials.

**The Airbrush and Spray Centre Ltd. 39 Littlehampton Road,
Worthing, Sussex BN13 1QJ**
Tel: 01903 830045

ALBA SUPPLIES & DISPOSABLES

Disposable latex gloves, cotton drill gloves, disposable aprons, oversleeves etc.

Alba Supplies & Disposables. P O Box 380, Chester CH4 8WE
Tel: 01244 659566

ANYTHING LEFT HANDED LTD

Dressmaking scissors, general scissors etc.

Anything Left Handed Ltd. 65 Beak Street, London W1

APPLICRAFT

Appliqué artists' glue in 56 colours and a clear glue for surface textile design, appliqué, art and craft work, that can be used on any surface. Washable.

Applicraft. 30A Platts Eyot, Lower Sunbury Road, Hampton, Middlesex TW12 2HF
Tel: 020 8979 7700 Fax: 020 8979 6600

ART DIRECT LTD

Art materials, airbrushes - mail order at discount prices.

Art Direct Ltd. 39 Littlehampton Road, Worthing BN13 1JQ

ART EXPRESS

Discounted textiles, craft and artists products available by mail order, plus free delivery UK mainland orders over £25.00. Call for free brochure. Craft paints, dyes, silk paints, silk fabrics, textile colours, silk colours, Thai tissue paper, watercolour papers, handmade papers and artists materials etc.

Art Express. Index House, 70 Burley Road, Leeds LS3 1JX
Tel: 0800 731 4185 Fax: 0113 243 6074

ARTISTS WORLD, UK

Products for silk and textile painting.

**Artists World, UK. The Wyevale Centre, Wareham Road, Owermoigne,
Nr Dorchester, Dorset DT2 8BY**
Tel: 01305 854099 Fax: 01305 854489

ARTS & INTERIORS

Silk paints, fabric paints and general craft products.

Arts & Interiors. 48 Princess Street, Yeovil
Tel: 01935 477790 Fax: 01935 434183

ART VAN GO

Exciting range of art and design materials.

Art Van Go. 16 Hollybush Lane, Datchworth, Knebworth, Hertfordshire SG3 6RE
Tel: 01438 814946 Fax: 01438 816267

ARTY'S

Discover the world of silk with ARTY'S.

ARTY'S. The Warehouse, 20 Reading Arch Road, Redhill, Surrey RH1 1HG
Tel: 01737 770446 Fax: 01737 770445

ASHILL COLOUR STUDIO

Mail order business specialising in natural dyes, dyestuff and equipment.

Ashill Colour Studio. 172 Clifton Road, Shefford, Bedfordshire SG17 5AH
Tel/Fax: 01462 812001

ATLAS CRAFT LTD

Deka range of paints, dyes, silk and fabric painting products for the retail market for stockists contact:

Atlas Craft Ltd. Thompson Street, Langley Mill, Nottingham NG16 4DE
Tel/Fax: 01773 761 444

BEADAZZLE

Assorted packs of handmade papers.

Beadazzle. 157 Westshaw Lane, Cudworth, Barnsley, South Yorkshire S72 8BL

BELDALE CRAFTS

Cold water soluble fabrics.

Beldale Crafts. 121 Raby Road, Hartlepool, Cleveland TS24 8DT

BEROL LTD

Fabric paints, pencil crayons, art equipment, paints etc.

Berol Ltd. Old Meadow Road, Kings Lynn, Norfolk PE30 4JR
Tel: 01553 761221

BRIGHT DESIGNS

Individual bead designs and "Uro Hot Set".

Bright Designs. 9 Penylan Lane, Oswestry, Shropshire SY11 2AQ

CANDLE MAKERS SUPPLIERS

Silk painting, wax and batik materials, including wax pots, tjantings, silk steamers, books and videos.

Candlemakers Suppliers. The Wax and Dyecraft Centre, 28 Blythe Road, London W14 OHA
Tel: 020 7602 4031 Fax: 020 7602 2796

CANNON (WHOLESALE) HABERDASHERY

Cash n' Carry/mail order specialist. Craft and haberdashery products.

Cannon (Wholesale) Haberdashery. 398-402 Langsett Road, Hillsboroug, Sheffield S6 2UG
Tel: 0114 232 5038

CATS GROUP

Mail order supplier of crafts, specialising in rugmaking kits, yarns, canvas and accessories. Deka silks and fabric paints, papermaking kits and craft accessories.

Cats Group. PO Box 12, Saxmundham IP17 3PB
Tel: 01728 648717 Fax: 01728 648593

CENTAGRAPH

All craft supplies. Mail order service.

Centagraph. 18 Station Parade, Harrogate, North Yorkshire HG1 1UE
Tel: 01423 566327

CHARTWELL GRAPH PAPER

Isometric Graph Paper.

H. W. Peel & Company Ltd. 1C Lyon Way, Rockware Estate, Greenford, Middlesex UB6 0BN
Tel: 020 8578 6861

CHOICES

General craft supplies and fabric products.

Choices. 36 Meadowside Road, Pangbourne, Reading, Berkshire RG8 7NH
Tel: 01734 843122

CHRISTINE HEUGHAN

Wet, ready, usable pulp dried cake colours, mounds, deckles and handmade papers. Summer schools and tuition available.

Christine Heughan. 3 Oxford Street, Edinburgh EH8 9PH
Tel: 0131 667 8728

COLOURCRAFT COLOURS & ADHESIVES LTD

Manufacturers and suppliers of a wide range of paints, marbling inks, fabric dyes and auxiliary products, brushes, colours and adhesives etc. Mail order and trade terms available.

Colourcraft Ltd. Unit 5, 555 Carlisle Street East, Sheffield S4 8DT
Tel: 0114 242 1431 Fax: 0114 242 1431

L. CORNELISSON & SON LTD

Worldwide mail order of artist materials, paints, brushes, papers, craft supplies, pigments, gilding supplies, easels and specialist decorating supplies.

L. Cornelisson & Son Ltd. 105 Great Russell Street, London WC1B 3RY
Tel: 020 7637 1045 Fax: 020 7636 3655

COWLING & WILCOX LTD

Stockists of fine art, craft and graphic materials, a comprehensive range of portfolios and display books. Mail order available. 10% discount to all full time students.

Cowling & Wilcox. 26-28 Broadwick Street, London W1V 1FG
Tel: 020 7734 9557 Fax: 020 7434 4513

CRAFT BASICS

Suppliers of needlework, Rowan Yarns, knitting and craft materials: beads, feathers, wires, unusual threads, fabric, silk paints etc. Mail order.

Craft Basics. 9 Gillygate, York YO31 7EA
Tel: 01904 652840 Fax: 01904 6528

CRAFT COLLECTION MILL SHOP

Craft retail specialist.

Craft Collection Mill Shop. Terry Mills, Westfield Road, Horbury, Wakefield WF46 6HE
Tel: 01924 811908

CRAFT CREATIONS LTD

General craft supplies. Mail order or visit Craft Creations Ltd. showrooms.

Craft Creations Ltd. Ingersoll House, Delamere Road, Cheshunt, Hertfordshire EN8 9HD
Tel: 01992 78190 Fax: 01992 634339

CRAFT DEPOT

Over 7000 craft items at retail and wholesale prices: needlework aids, felt, paper crafts, jewellery findings, glue and glue guns, ribbons, lace, plastic canvases, paint, wearable art, books etc. Catalogue £4.00 refundable when spending £20.00 or more. Exclusively mail order.

Craft Depot. Unit 6, Somerton Business Park, Somerton, Somerset TA11 6SB
Tel: 01458 274727 Fax: 01458 272932

DAINTY SUPPLIES LTD

Wholesale, retail and mail order: crafts, haberdashery, craft fabrics, fur fabrics, wadding, foam and bridalwear fabrics.

Dainty Supplies Ltd. Unit 35, Phoenix Road, Crowther Industrial Estate, District 3. Washington, Tyne & Wear NE38 0AD
Tel: 0191 416 7886 Fax: 0191 417 6277

DALER-ROWNEY LTD

Art and craft materials.

Daler-Rowney Ltd. Bracknell, Berkshire RG12 8ST
Tel: 01344 4244621 Fax: 01344 486511

DYLON INTERNATIONAL LTD

Manufacturer of consumer fabric dyes and fabric paints.

Dylon International Ltd. Worsley Bridge Road, Lower Sydenham, London SE26 5HD
Tel: 020 8663 4801 Fax: 020 8658 6735

EATON'S SEASHELLS

Miniature and small shells: drilled shells available. Flat mother of pearl for inlay and antique restoration.

Eaton's Seashells. 30 Forest Drive West, London E11 1LA
Tel/Fax: 020 8539 5288

EDDING (UK) INTERNATIONAL

Trade distributors for the "Marabu" range of silk and fabric paints, dyes and Edding textile markers. For stockist details contact: Tel: 01727 846688

Edding (UK) Ltd. Merlin Centre, Acrewood Way, St. Albans, Hertfordshire AL4 0JY
Tel: 01727 846688 Fax: 01727 839970

THE FABRIC COLOUR WORKSHOP

Silk painting and glass painting kits and supplies, equipment and accessories. ARTY'S silk and cotton ranges, silk, velvet plain and devoré scarves by the metre. Lectures, demonstrations and workshops. Mail order available.

The Fabric Colour Workshop. 91 Fleetgate, Barton-on-Humber, North Lincolnshire DN18 5QD
Tel/Fax: 01652 636318

FALKINERS

Handmade fine papers.

Falkiners. 111 Long Acre, London
Tel: 020 7831 1151

FASHION N' FOIL MAGIC

Suppliers of foils and adhesives for the textile and paper printing industries. Easy to use with video instruction. Also specialist adhesives to use with the foils. Mail order service send large SAE.

Fashion n' Foil Magic. PO Box 3746, London N2 9DE
Tel: 020 8444 1992 Fax: 020 8883 084

FIBRECRAFTS
Leading supplier in Europe for textile arts: Spinning, weaving, fibres and yarns, books, equipment, wheels, looms, dyestuffs and chemicals for dyeing and batik. International mail order suppliers.

Fibre Crafts. 1 Old Portsmouth Road, Peasmarsh, Guildford, Surrey GU3 1LZ
Tel: 01483 421853 Fax: 01483 419960 e-mail: Fybrecraft@aol.com

FISKARS UK LTD
Fiskars Uk Ltd. Bridgend Business Centre, Bridgend, Mid Glamorgan CF31 3XJ
Tel: 01656 655595 Fax: 01656 659582

FLORAKITS
Wholesale and retail suppliers of art, craft, floral and hobby materials. A wide range of products for all floral and craft applications: silk and dried flowers, artist supplies and ribbons. Mail order division dispatching orders worldwide.

Florakits. Worrall Street, Congleton, Cheshire CW12 1DT
Tel: 01260 271371

FRAMECRAFT MINIATURES LTD
Manufacturers and distributors of over 300 products and accessories that can be completed with craft and needlework designs. Mail order catalogue - send 4 x 1st class stamps.

Framecraft Miniatures Ltd. 372-376 Summer Lane, Hockley, Birmingham B19 3QA
Tel: 0121 212 0551 Fax: 0121 212 0552

FRED ALDOUS LTD
A huge choice of quality materials for arts, crafts and hobbies. Mail order catalogue available send 2 x 1st class stamps.

Fred Aldous Ltd. PO Box 135, 37 Lever Street, Manchester M1 1LW
Tel: 0161 236 2477 Fax: 0161 236 6075 www.fredaldous.co.uk

HANTEX LTD
Distributors of quilting and general needlecraft products: fabrics, muslin, craft books, buttons, Kunin felt, notions etc. Wholesale only.

Hantex Ltd. Tel: 01908 511331 Fax: 01908 511055

HANDEZE (UK) LTD
Handeze Therapeutic Gloves designed to alleviate pains beneficial for stitchers, knitters, quilters, lacemakers, painters, machinists etc.

Handeze (UK) Ltd. Nathan Court, Redbrook Lane, Brereton, Rugeley, Staffordshire WS15 1QU
Tel: 0889 576171

HOBBIES & HANDICRAFTS
Suppliers of a wide range of craft materials by mail order or to the trade.

Hobbies and Handicrafts. Warners Mill, 24-26 South Street, Braintree, Essex CM7 3HA
Tel: 01376 55009 Fax: 01376 551177

HOBBY CRAFT

Fantasy film.

Hobby Craft. Handicraft House, Notley Road, Braintree, Essex CM7 1GB
Tel: 01376 347000

HOMECRAFT

Needlecraft products: Anchor, DMC embroidery threads, Framecraft, Heritage, embroidery seed beads, beadwork kits and many types of beads. Mail order only.

Homecraft. 16 Crescent Parade, Uxbridge Road, Uxbridge, Middlesex UB10 0LG
Tel: 01895 238152 Fax: 01895 847954

HOMECRAFT DIRECT

Natural jutes - 5ply and 7ply, wooden rings, beads and leather thonging. Catalogue available.

Homecraft Direct. PO Box 30, Leicester LE1 9BU
Tel: 0116 251 3139

THE HOME HABERDASHERY

Extensive range of haberdashery and craft supplies.

The Home Haberdashery. PO Box 5531, Nottingham NG5 4BF

THE HOUSE OF HANDICRAFTS

Art, craft and hobby supplies. Marbling sets, tube beads, fabric painting sets, silk painting sets, fantasy film, glitter powders, decorative sprays, paper and card, foil, metallized crepes etc.

The House of Handicrafts. Silks Way, Warners Mill, Braintree, Essex CM7 3HA
Tel: 01376 550099 Fax: 01376 551177

JAKAR INTERNATIONAL LTD

Pastels, watersoluble and permanent colours, gouache, watercolours, Techno-graphic, art materials etc.

Jakar International Ltd. Hillside House, 2-6 Friern Park, London N12 9BX
Tel: 020 8445 2714

JAMES CROPPER

Manufacturer of papers and boards.

James Cropper. Burnside Mills, Kendal, Cumbria LA9 6PZ
Tel: 01539 722002

J. A. MILTON

Upholstery supplies.

J. A. Milton. Unit 6, Whitchurch Business Park, Whitchurch, Shropshire SY13 1LJ
Tel: 01948 663434 Fax: 01948 665560

JANIK LTD

Leathers, paints, stencils, book, videos etc.

Janik Ltd. Brickfield Lane, Ruthin, Denbighshire, North Wales LL15 2TN

JUST CRAFTS WHOLESALE LTD
Large selection of trimmings, frillings, nets, tulle, tapestry and embroidery kits.
Just Crafts Wholesale Ltd. Stitchery House, Chalford, Stroud, Gloucestershire GL6 8HN
Tel: 01453 886575

INSCRIBE LTD
Fabric prints.
Inscribe Ltd. The Woolmer Industrial Estate, Bordon, Hampshire GU35 9QE
Tel: 01420 475747

KALEN CRAFTS
DMC main agents, Anchor, Disney, Framecraft, cross stitch, embroidery threads, kits and accessories.
Kalen Crafts. 5 Springfield Centre, Orchard Street, Kempston, Bedfordshire MK42 7PY
Tel: 01234 843323 Fax: 01234 855966

KUNDALINI PAPERMAKER
Papermaker kits. The kits include full instructions. Mail order.
Kundalini Papermaker. Clifton, Strathblane, Glasgow G63 9EX
Tel: 0780 127 1027

LAZERTRAN LTD
Specialist transfer paper for artists, crafts people, the fashion industry, tapestry, needlepoint, embroidery and all the textile arts transferring any image onto any surface. Telephone for advice and assistance.
Lazertran Ltd. Ardwyn, Aberarth, Aberaeron, Ceredigion SA46 0LX
Tel: 0154 5571 149

LEANDA
Manufacturers of textile craft equipment. Supplying mail order to spinners, weavers, embroiderers, textile artists and crafts people worlwide. Specialists in Japanese braiding and tassel making.
Leanda. Scotts Yard, Ber Street, Norwich NR1 3HA
Tel: 01603 763340 Fax: 01603 765314

LEICESTER LAMINATING SERVICES
Plastic, graph and template material.
Leicester Laminating Services. 71 Westfield Road, Weston Park, Leicester LE3 6HU

MATRIX MOULDINGS
Liquid latex.
Matrix Mouldings. New Barns, Brook End Road, Chelmsford, Essex CM2 6PA
Tel: 01245 466322

MIDDLEBROOKS CRAFT WORLD

Art and crafts equipment, needlecrafts, ribbons, buttons, beads, trims, paints, papers, cards etc.

Middlebrooks Craft World. 31-33 The Linkway, Middlebrook Leisure Park, Bolton, Lancashire
Tel: 01204 469770

M. J. J. TRIMCRAFT

Educational suppliers to the art and craft section. Sequins, beads, buttons, ribbons, collage materials, trimmings, haberdashery, papier mâché, holographic paper and many more trimmings.

M. J. J. Trimcraft. Trimcraft House, 100 Spring Hall Lane, Halifax HX1 4TW
Tel: 01422 381723 Fax: 01422 381725

MULBERRY PAPERS

Exotic range of handmade papers.

Mulberry Papers. 2 Old Rectory Cottages, Easton Grey, Malmesbury, Wiltshire SN16 0PE
Tel/Fax: 01666 841023

NES ARNOLD

Art, textile, design and technology equipment and craft materials.

NES Arnold. Ludlow Hill Road, West Bridgford, Nottingham NG2 6HD
Tel: 0115 9452201 Fax: 0500 410420

OPITEC - EDUCATIONAL MATERIALS LTD

Art materials, encaustic art, needlecrafts, silk painting materials, tools, accessories for a wide range of art and craft activities.

Opitec - Educational Materials Ltd. 7 West Road, Woolston, Southampton SO19 9AH
Tel: 01703 446515 Fax 01703 446991

PANDURO HOBBY

Mail order supplier of over 13000 craft items.

Panduro Hobby. Freepost, Transport Avenue, Brentford, Middlesex TW8 8BR
Tel: 01392 427788 (24 hrs) Fax: 020 8847 5073

THE PAPER SHED

Wide range of handcrafted papers produced from natural materials, many hand dyed. Sold by mail order. Choose from silk, plants, metallics, tissues or buy a kit to make your own. Silk papers a speciality. Mail order.

The Paper Shed. March House, Tollerton, York YO61 1QQ
Tel: 01347 838253 Fax: 01347 838096

PAPETERIE

Handmade art papers, collage packs, boxes and bags.

Papeterie. 35 Market Place, Kingston Upon Thames KT1 1JQ
Tel: 020 8546 0313 Fax: 029 8546 0525

PAPYRUS

Selection of art papers available from:

Papyrus. 48 Fulham Road, London SW3 6HH
Tel: 020 7584 8022
and also 8 Upper Borough Walls, Bath BA1 IRG
Tel: 01225 463418 Fax: 01225 460 262

PARCHMENT EXPRESS

Quality papers, parchment craft papers.

Parchment Express. Magmaker Ltd. Cromwell Court, St Ives, Cambridgeshire PE17 4BG
Tel: 01204 469770

PAUL DAY

Manufacturers of silk, textile paints and markers. Agents for Bodson-Nelis & Cie, Belgium.

Paul Day. 23 Fallowfield, Ampthill, Bedford MK45 2TS
Tel: 01525 403357 Fax: 01525 840057

PEARCE TANDY LEATHERCRAFT LTD

Full range of leathercraft tools, kits, dyes, buckles, leathers, patterns, videos, books and hardware. Also Indian lore supplies including feathers, beads, hairpipes, sinew etc. Retail shop and mail order service.

Pearce Tandy Leathercraft Ltd. Billing Park, Northampton NN3 9BG
Tel: 01604 407177 Fax: 01604 407561

PENTEL (STATIONERY) LTD

Artists materials, drawing and writing instruments, bold vivid colours to subtle, sophisticated hues. Graphic markers, fine liners, pastel dye sticks, watercolours, technical pens, fabric markers, paint markers etc.

Pentel (Stationery) Ltd Hunts Rise, South Marston Park, Swindon, Wiltshire SW3 4TW
Tel: 01793 823333 Fax: 01793 823366

PERIVALE-GÜTERMANN LTD

Embroidery threads, materials and equipment.

Perivale-Gütermann Ltd. Wadsworth Road, Greenford, Middlesex, UB6 7JS
Tel: 0181 998 5000 Fax: 0181 991 1344

PHRAZZLE CARD

Quality cards and papers in 70 colours and 12 textures.

Phrazzle Cards. Unit 37, Trinity Enterprise Centre, Furness Business Park, Barrow in Furness, Cumbria LA14 2PN
Tel/Fax: 01229 838700

PLASTI-KOTE

Specialists in spray and stencil paints. Available in most DIY stores.

Plasti-kote. London Road Industrial Estate, Sawston, Cambridge, Cambridgeshire CB2 4TP
Tel: 01223 836400

RAINBOW SILKS

Specialist supplier of surface decoration, textile and silk painting materials.
Dyes, paints, fabrics, etc. Send SAE for mail order details.

Rainbow Silks. 27 New Road, Amersham, Buckinghamshire HP6 6LD
Tel: 01494 727003 Fax: 01494 724101

ROYAL SOVEREIGN LTD

Manufacturers and distributors of art, craft and design materials: textile paints, mosaic tiles,
wire form, modelling mesh, colour shaper artists modelling tools etc.

Royal Sovereign Ltd. 7 St George's Industrial Estate, White Hart Lane, London N22 5QL
Tel: 020 8888 6888 Fax: 020 8888 7029

SARAH MAY DESIGNS LTD

Range of pewter needlework accessories, pincushions, scissor and needle cases.
Range of counted thread embroidery kits, cross stitch, hardanger, blackwork etc.

Sarah May Designs Ltd. 5 Pettiphers Farm, Dorsington Lane, Pebworth CV37 8AW
Tel/Fax: 01789 720617

SHEBA BLADES

Sharpening and replacement blades service.

Sheba Blades. Flint Cottage, Treacle Lane, Rushden, Buntingford, SG9 0SL

SILK PAINTING CENTRE

Mail order company supplying materials for silk painting, maribou, Pebo, ARTY'S and many
more. Steaming service. Weekly classes and Saturday workshops. Free catalogue.

Silk Painting Centre. Nobles Barn, Blendworth, Hordean, Hampshire PO8 0AH
Tel/Fax: 01705 598861

SMALLWARES LTD

Knit weave needles.

Smallwares Ltd. 17 Galena Road, King Street, Hammersmith, London W6 0LN

SMITCRAFT

Mail order specialist offering art, craft and needlework supplies: shells, beads, rugmaking,
embroidery equipment and accessories. 152 page full colour catalogue.

Smitcraft. Unit 1, Eastern Road, Aldershot, Hampshire GU12 4TE
Tel: 01252 342626 (24hrs)

SPECIALIST CRAFT LTD

Mail order supplier of over 9000 craft/textile items including screen printing supplies.

Specialist Craft Ltd. PO Box 247, Leicester LE1 9QS
Tel: 0116 251 0405 Fax: 0116 251 5015

STAEDTLER (UK) LTD

Ranges from Staedtler include: Karat Aquarell pencils, Karat Aquarell crayons, Karat Liqua
watersoluble liquid wax, "Easy Metal", an easy technique surfaces with leaf metal. Idea and
colour range of paints. General art materials.

Staedtler (UK) Ltd. Pontyclun, Mid Glamorgan CF72 8YJ
Tel: 01443 237421 Fax: 01443 237440

STICKY FINGERS

Mail order suppliers of self adhesives, felts and flocks. Manufacturers of water based paints and adhesives suitable for a variety of uses including fabrics.

Sticky Fingers. 19 Mill Lane, Coppull, Chorley, Lancashire PR7 5AW
Tel: 01257 792509 Fax: 01257 793196

SUE HILEY

Mail order service offering silk fibres, wadding, ribbon, dyes, fabric, yarn and related books. Silk products for handspinners, handweavers, quilters, embroiderers, needleworkers and silk devotees.

Sue Hiley. The Mill, Tregoyd Mill, Three Cocks, Brecon, Powys, Wales LD3 0SW
Tel/Fax: 01497 847421

TEACHING ART

Kopykate drawing projectors: Kwikdraw and various other designs.

Teaching Art. PO Box 50, Newark, Nottingham NG23 5GY

TELFORDS

Mail order suppliers of craft materials, specialising in bead packs.

Telfords. 25 Orpington Road, Winchmore Hill, London N21 3PD
Tel: 020 8882 7729

TERRY TAYLOR ASSOCIATES

Fabric paints.

Terry Taylor Associates. 27 Woodland Road, Tunbridge Wells, Kent TN4 9HW

TEXTILE EXPRESSION

Embroidery and textile products by mail order including handmade papers, colouring media, fabrics from hessian to velvet, cotton, ready to dye, paint or print.
Fabrics for contemporary design. Dyes and colouring media. Handmade papers and decorative threads. Mail order catalogue available.

Textile Expression. 31 Belmont Road, Burton-on-Trent, Tutbury, Staffordshire DE13 9NL
Tel: 01283 520496 Fax: 01283 520878

TOLLIT & HARVEY LTD

Manufacturers/UK distributors of a wide range of art and craft products, including comprehensive ranges of art materials, paints, pastels, brushes, portfolios, pads, paper, coloured card and board. Stockists lists available.

Tollit & Harvey Ltd. Oldmeadow Road, King's Lynn, Norfolk PE30 4LW
Tel: 01553 696600 Fax: 01553 767235

TOPAZ CRAFTS

Stockists of a wide range of craft and hobby materials. UK stockists of "Jones Tones" fabric paints and accessories. Catalogue available, plus technique booklet.

Topaz Crafts. Oswaldtwistle Mill, Collier Street, Oswaldtwistle, Accrington, Lancashire BB5 3DF
Tel: 01254 770702/3 Fax: 01254 770703

TRYLON LTD

Silicon rubber, latex, gelflex.

Trylon Ltd. Thrift Street, Wollaston, Northants NN29 7QJ
Tel: 01933 664275

VYCOMBE ARTS

Silk fabric, paints, dyes (including Procion), transfer paints, silk, embroidery threads, foils, glitter dust, embroidery puff paints, acrylic craft paints, Guttas, Carragheen for marbling, silks by the metre etc. dissolvable fabrics, plus much more. Catalogue available. 2 x 1st class stamps. Mail order service.

Vycombe Arts. Fen Way, Fen Walk, Woodbridge, Suffolk IP12 4AS
Tel/Fax: 01394 380882

WAKES WAXES

Encaustic art supplies, wax blocks and beeswax based sticks - coloured with non toxic natural pigments, plus gold, silver and clear.

Wakes Waxes. Loveneys Farm, Wakes Colne, Colchester C06 2BJ
Tel: 01787 227320 Fax: 01787 228309

WARD ART & CRAFTY WAREHOUSE

Art and craft materials, supplies and equipment.

Ward Art and Crafty Warehouse. Halifax Road, Dunston Industrial Estate, Gateshead, Tyne and Wear NE11 9HV
Tel: 0191 460 5915

W. G. BALL LTD

Lead free jewellery enamels and accessory suppliers.

W. G. Ball Ltd. Anchor Road, Longton, Staffordshire ST3 1JW

WHYKRAFT PRODUCTS

Craft products. Mail order available.

Whykraft Products. Tarrant way, Moulton, Northampton NN3 7US

WIRES COMPANY. UK

Metal and covered wires of all descriptions for craft, educational, electrical, hobby and electronic applications. The scientific wire company.

Wires Company UK. 18 Raven Road, London E18 1HW
Tel: 020 8505 0002 Fax: 020 8559 1114

WOOL N' THINGS & CROCHET TOO

Yarns, crochet accessories, haberdashery, embroidery threads etc.

Wool n' Things & Crochet Too. 248 Shawfield Road, Ash, Nr Aldershot, Hampshire GU16 5DJ
Tel/Fax: 01252 334855

ANTIQUE FABRIC CLEANING

Cleaners of old fabrics.

Antique Fabric Cleaning. 349-351 Aylsham Road, Norwich, Norfolk NR3 2RX
Tel/Fax: 01603 300085

DE HAVILAND EMBROIDERY

Individually hand dyed embroidery threads, specially dyed for conservation and restoration work. Mail order only.

De Haviland Embroidery. Monomark House, 27 Old Gloucester Street, London WC1 3XX
Tel: 020 7289 2123

THE FAN MUSEUM

The Craft Workshop at The Fan Museum undertakes the conservation and restoration of fans - by appointment.

The Fan Museum. 12 Crooms Hill, Greenwich, London SE10 8ER
Tel: 020 8858 7879 or 020 8305 1441 Fax: 020 8293 1889

KYSNIA MARKO TEXTILE CONSERVATION WORKSHOP

Unit 39, Limehouse Cut, Morris Road, London E14

RESTORE PRODUCTS

Specialist textile conservation materials including cleaning and rust removal kits, extra fine needles, threads, silk crepeline, acid-free tissue and storage boxes. Mail order.

Restore Products. 2 Talbot Road, Bowdon, Altrincham, Cheshire WA14 3JD
Tel/Fax: 0161 928 0020

THE ROYAL SCHOOL OF NEEDLEWORK

25 Princes Gate, London SW7

TEXTILE CLEANING & CONSERVATION

Specialists in cleaning and conserving historic textiles, including embroidery, printed and painted textiles, upholstery, lace, costume, and accessories with advice on textile cleaning and conservation.

Textile Cleaning & Conservation. 271 Sandown Road, Deal, Kent CT14 6OU
Tel: 01304 373684 Fax: 01304 363784

TEXTILE CONSERVATION CENTRE

Apartment 22, Hampton Court Palace, East Molesey, Surrey KT8 9AU
Tel: 020 8977 4943

THE TEXTILE RESTORATION STUDIO

The studio cleans, conserves or repairs antique tapestry, lace, ermbroidery, costume, church vestments and furnishings etc.

The Textile Restoration Studio. Altrincham, Cheshire WA14 3JD
Tel/Fax: 0161 928 0020

BLACK SHEEP WOOLS

15 Wigan Galleries, The Galleries, Wigan, Lancashire WN1 1AR
Tel: 01942 825130

BOB TAILS

Handspun fibres including: angora, fleece, camel, silk etc and private commissions undertaken to spin and knit fleece: dog, cat and other pet fibres from your own pets.

Bob Tails. 220 Seaside Road, Aldbrough, Nr Hull, East Yorkshire HU11 4RY
Tel: 01964 527801

BONNIE'S WOOLS LTD

1273 Bristol Road South, Northfield, Birmingham B31 2SP
Tel: 0121 475 1691 Fax: 0121 478 2197

F. W. BRAMWELL YARNS & CO LTD

Wholesale suppliers of coned yarns to the home machine and handknitting enthusiast and craft trade. Worldwide distributors for yarns, pattern books and designs.

F. W. Bramwell & Co. Ltd. Unit 8B, Simestone Business Park, Blackburn Road, Simonstone, Burnley, Lancashire BB12 7NQ
Tel: 01282 779811 Fax: 01282 779860

BRITISH MOHAIR SPINNERS

Specialities in natural fibres for weaving, machine and handknitting. mohair, alpaca, wool, silk and synthetic blends.

British Mohair Spinners. Lower Holme, Ottley Road, Basildon, Shipley, West Yorkshire BD17 7EU
el: 01274 583111

BROCKWELL YARNS

Copley Marshall & Company Ltd. Wildspur Mills, New Mills, Huddersfield HD7 7ET
Tel: 01484 682306

BRYNKIR WOOLLEN MILL

Welsh black and white yarns.

Brynkir Woollen Mill. Golan, Garn-Dolbenmaen, Gwynedd

BSK LTD - (BEDFORD SEWING & KNITTING CENTRE LTD)

Knitting machines, tools, equipment, spares and accessories etc. Forsell, Yeoman, Bonnie's, Amber yarns etc. Worldwide mail order service, free catalogue available. Large warehouse and showroom open to visitors.

BSK Ltd. Murdock Road, Manton Industrial Estate, Bedford MK41 7LE
Tel: 01234 217096 Fax: 01234 271537

BUSBY YARNS

PO Box 930, Dundonald, Kilmarnock, Ayrshire, Scotland KA2 9BH
Tel/Fax: 01563 850981

BUTTERFLY DIRECT LTD

Machine/handknitters 4ply cones.

Butterfly Direct Ltd. 17/21 Leeds Road, Windhills, Shipley, West Yorkshire BD18 1BP
Tel/Fax: 01274 741500

CAPRICORN MOHAIR LTD

"From Kid to Cone to Ball" Mohair blend yarns. Superfine 4ply and chunky yarns.

Capricorn Mohair Ltd. Manor Farm, Chadwell, Melton Mowbray, Leicestershire LE14 4QL
Tel: 01664 444570 Fax: 01664 444642

CELANDINE LTD.

Established mail order supplier of exclusive luxury yarns, mainly in natural fibres, to the home knitter and designer knitwear companies. Silk blends, linen blends, Shetland wool, kid mohair and pattern books.

Celandine Ltd. Unit 7, Drill Hall Business Centre, East Parade, Ilkley, West Yorkshire
Tel: 01943 604440 Fax: 01943 604441

COLDHARBOUR MILL WORKING WOOL MUSEUM

Producing pure wool 3ply, double knitting and Aran yarns, spun on site in an attractive range of designer colours. Also home and Devon Tartan in original green and companion blue.

Coldharbour Mill Working Wool Museum. Coldharbour Mill,
Uffculme, Cullompton, Devon EX15 3EE
Tel: 01884 840960 Fax: 01884 840858

COLDSPRING MILL

Retail and wholesale discount knitting yarns. A vast stock of hand and machine knitting yarns from top spinners, all at greatly reduced prices. Stock is constantly changing, so a visit to the mill is recommended. Trade enquiries welcome.

Coldspring Mill. Haworth Road, Cullingworth, Bradford, West Yorkshire BD13 5EE
Tel: 01535 275646

COLINETTE YARNS LTD

Haberdashery, trimmings, chenille and other yarns.

Colinette Yarns Ltd. Units 2-5 Industrial Workshops, Llanfair, Caerienion,
Powys, Wales SY21 0SG
Tel: 01938 810128 Fax: 01938 810127

COPLEY MARSHALL & COMPANY LTD

Yarn dyers, bleachers, mercerisers, winders and producers of natural and manmade yarns for hand and machine knitting, narrow fabrics and apparel available.

Copley Marshall & Company Ltd. Wildspur Mill, New Mill, Huddersfield HD7 7ET
Tel: 01484 682306 Fax: 01484 684970

COURTAULDS SPINNING

Courtaulds Spinning. PO Box 100, 1 Portland Street, Manchester M60 3AP
Tel: 0161 236 8466

CREATIVITY

Needlecraft specialists: tapestry, yarns, embroidery etc.

45 New Oxford Street, London WC1 and Downing Street, Farnham, Surrey.
Tel: 020 7240 2945 Fax: 020 7240 6030

CYGNET WOOLS LTD

Distributors to the retail industry: acrylics, wool/nylon mixes, 3ply to chunky.

Cygnet Wools Ltd. 12 Adelaide Street, Bradford, West Yorkshire BD5 OEF
Tel: 01274 743374 Fax: 01274 732233

DENYS BRUNTON DESIGNER YARNS

Victoria Mill, Station Road, Turton, Bolton, Lancashire BL7 OHB
Tel/Fax: 01204 852604

DESIGNER YARNS

A wide range of Merino, lamb's wool and pure cotton yarns on cone for designers. Large and small quantities available. All yarns available by mail order. Shade cards and price list available on request, send £1.00 refundable with order.

Designer Yarns. P.O. Box 18, Long Croft, Keighley, West Yorkshire BD21 5AU
Tel: 01535 680305 Fax: 01535 600531

EVERGREEN - J. P. TEXTILES

Re-cycled luxury yarns; silk/cashmere, Aran weight yarns etc. available.

Evergreen. 13 Maltkin Row, Cawthorne, Barnsley, South Yorkshire
Tel/Fax: 01226 791358

EWENIQUE

Quality pure wool yarns in natural wool colours or in a range of dyed yarns. Mail order.

Ewenique. 32 Ashley Road, Aberdeen AB1 6RJ

FIL d' OR

Importers and distributors in the UK of Bouton D' Or French Knitting Yarn and other knitting yarns.

Fil d' Or. 20 High Street, Droitwich, Worcester WR9 8EW
Tel/Fax: 01905 776793

FOCUS NEEDLECRAFTS

Cash and carry or mail order. Branded and unbranded knitting wools, needlecraft and yarns for knitting, crochet, spinning, cross stitch and needlework. Also fabrics, haberdashery, canvas, kits, patterns and sewing threads. Mail order delivery service throughout the UK.

Focus Needlecrafts. Unit 4, Elm Court, Crystal Drive, Sandwell Business Park, Smethwick, West Midlands B66 1RB
Tel: 0121 552 5035 Fax: 0121 544 9699

T. FORSELL & SON LTD

Forsell & Son Ltd. Blaby Road, South Wigston, Leicester LE8 2SG
Tel: 0116 2786281

FRANGIPANI KNITWEAR

Available on cone in twelve colours, specialist Guernsey high quality 5ply wool suppliers, suitable for both standard gauge machine knitting and hand knitting. Mail order or personal callers - trade on request or retail small amounts welcome.

Frangipani Knitwear. Meaver Farm, Mullion, Cornwall TR12 7DN
Tel: 01326 240128 Fax: 01326 240011

GARDINER OF SELKIRK LTD

Stock service, woolmark, woollen spun yarns for knitting and weaving.

Gardiner of Selkirk Ltd. Tweed Mills, Selkirk, Scotland TD7 5NA
Tel: 01750 20283 Fax: 01750 22525

THE GOAT COMPANY

Pure mohair products from our own angora goats, fabric with matching yarns. Pure mohair dyed to order. Pure kid, mohair/lambswool, kid/silk, Capri-Laine.

The Goat Company. Daren Farm, Llanvynoe, Longtown, Herefordshire HR2 ONG
Tel: 01873 860240

GREGORY KASSAPIAN & PARTNERS LTD.

Aran wool, knitting books.

Gregory Kassapian & Partners Ltd. Spring Mill House, Shipley, West Yorkshire BD17 6AD
Tel: 01274 586271 Fax: 01274 531680

HARTINGTON YARNS

Acrylic 4ply, fine ply, 2/14 brushed, double knits, crepe acrylic/wool blends etc.

Hartington Yarns. Plot 7, Unit 2B, Eagle Road, Quarry Hill Industrial park, Ilkestone, Derbyshire DE7 4RB
Tel/Fax: 0115 922 3654

HAYFIELD TEXTILES LTD

Plain and fancy knit yarns.

Hayfield Textiles Ltd. Flanshaw Lane, Alverthorpe, Wakefield, West Yorkshire WF2 9ND
Tel: 01924 371501 Fax: 01924 290506

HILARY CHETWYND

Silk weaving yarns.

Hilary Chetwynd. Kipping Cottage, Cheriton, Alresford, Hampshire S024 0PN

HUMPHRIES WEAVING COMPANY LTD

Handloom silk weavers. Commission yarn dyers and suppliers. Yarn sales: silk, cottons, linen, wool from stock. Mail order available. Also suppliers of handwoven silk fabrics 20 metres - minimum order lengths.

Humphries Weaving Company Ltd. Devere Mill, Queen Street, Castle Hedingham, Halstead, Essex CO9 3HA
Tel: 01787 461193 Fax: 01787 462701

HUNTERS OF BRORA LTD
Knitting yarns, apparel fabrics in wool, silk and linens.

Hunters of Brora. Sutherland, Scotland KW9 6NA
Tel: 01408 623500 Fax: 01408 623533

HUSH KNIT YARNS
Specialists in yarns for home knitting machine market, either to the retail section or direct to the customer by mail order.

Hush Knit Yarns. 57 Burnside Drive, Bramcote Hills, Beeston, Nottingham NG9 3EF
Tel/Fax: 0115 922 3654

JAEGER HANDKNITS
Jaeger Handknits. Green Lane Mill, Holmfirth, West Yorkshire HD7 IRW
Tel: 01484 680050

JAMIESON & SMITH-SHETLAND WOOL BROKERS LTD
Buyer of the Shetland Islands Wool Clip, offering a most extensive colour range of Shetland knitting yarns in many weights on hank and cone. From 1ply cobweb fine through to Heavy Unst Fleece. Produced in Shetland from the local crofters and farmers. Also exclusive knitting packs for all the family. Large SAE for illustrated brochure. World-wide mail order.

Jamieson & Smith - Shetland Wool Brokers Ltd. 90 North Road, Lerwick, Shetland ZE1 0PQ
Tel: +44 (0)1595 693579 Fax: +44 (0)1595 695009

JÓNA SPAREY
The Icelandic Tapestry School, suppliers of Lopi wool, Létti Lopi - mail order only.

Jóna Sparey. The Icelandic Tapestry School, Southleigh,
Langport Road, Somerton, Somerset TA11 6RT
Tel: 01458 273111

KING COLE LTD.
King Cole Ltd. Merrie Mills, Brigg Street, Crossflatts, Bingley, West Yorkshire BD16 2AX
Tel: 01274 561331 Fax: 01274 551095

KNITTERS BY POST
Top branded yarns.

Knitters by Post. 116 Sunbridge Road, Bradford BD1 2NF

LISTER YARNS
Lister Yarns. Midlands Office, Abbey Mills, Ross Walk, Leicester LE4 5HH
Tel: 0116 251 5678 Fax: 0116 251 5679

THE LUREX COMPANY LTD
1 Harewood Row, London NW1 6SE
Tel: 020 7258 0138

MARGARET PIERS

Wool, cotton mix, wool/acrylic and high sheen Draylon yarns. Please send £3.00 for shade cards.

Margaret Piers. 51-53 Lancaster Road, Hindley, Wigan, Lancashire WN2 3NJ
Tel: 01942 255958

MERCIA WOOLS - CASH & CARRY

Handknitting yarn manufacturers and wholesalers of crafts and haberdashery.

Mercia Wools - Cash & Carry. 19 Lythalls Lane, Folleshill, Coventry CV6 6FN
Tel/Fax: 01203 686079

MERRIHAY

Quality yarns from home grown natural fibres. Wool, cashmere etc.

Merrihay Fibres. Poole Farm, Grosmont, Abergavenny, Monmouthshire NP7 8HU

THE NATURAL FIBRE COMPANY LTD

Yarn design for knitwear designers. Contract spinning from 20Kg to 500Kg. Natural coloured rare and regional wools in blends with mohair and silk, Cashgora, Wensleydale/silk, hand dyed yarns from lace weights to chunkies.

The Natural Fibre Company Ltd. 12 Llambed Enterprise Park, Lampeter SA48 8LT
Tel: 01570 422956 Fax: 01570 481075

NEEDLECRAFT DIRECT

Assorted yarns.

Needlecraft Direct. 14 Maylord, Orchards, Hereford HR1 2DS

NINA A. MIKLAN

Designer Yarns: 100% Merino wool, super kid, silk/cashmere/alpaca wool blends.

Nina A. Miklin PO Box 1720, London W9 1TT
Tel: 020 7286 1532

PAINTBOX YARNS LTD

All natural fibre knitting yarns: pure new wool, silk, alpaca, cotton chenille, cotton/linen, wool/silk blends, mohair, chunkiest Aran, to 1ply quality and many more, suitable for hand and machine knitting. Mail order only. Shade cards available at £3.50 inclusive carriage + VAT. Extensive colour range.

Paintbox Yarns Ltd. 15 Bramwood Close, Carshalton, Surrey SM5 1PQ
Tel: 020 8669 2950 Fax: 020 7773 8494

PAMELA WISE

Pamela Wise. 101 - 105 Goswell Road, London EC1V 7ER
Tel: 020 7490 0037

PAPILLION

Luxury mohair.

Papillion. Hollings Mill, Lower Grattan Road, Bradford BD1 2JA
Tel: 01274 727283 Fax: 01274 304042

PATONS
Black Rock Mills. Linthwaite, Huddersfield, West Yorkshire HD7 5NT
Tel: 01484 537900

PATRICIA ROBERTS
Designer yarns.
60 Kinnerton Street, London SW1X 8ES
Tel: 020 7235 4742 Fax: 020 7235 6577

PEERLESS YARNS
Wool, cotton mix, wool/acrylic and high sheen draylon yarns. Please send £3 for shade cards.
Peerless Yarns. 51-53 Lancster Road, Hindley, Wigan, Lancashire WN2 3NJ
Tel: 01942 255958

PINGOU CARLISLE
Major stockists of Phildar and Pingouin yarns. Mail order service available.
Pingouin Carlisle. 20 Globe Lane, Carlisle CA3 8NX
Tel: 01228 520681

RAINBOW'S END YARNS
Hand dyed English mohair, Wenslydale woollen yarns, soft, smooth and highly individual yarns. Exsquisite silk yarns from Japan. Undyed and dyed yarns.
Rainbow's End Yarns. Ivy House, Dennington Road, Framlingham, Suffolk IP13 9UL

RENNIE & CO.
Shetland supersoft, lambswool/alpaca, lambswool and silk.
Rennie & Co. Milladen, Mintlaw, Peterhead AB42 65A Scotland
Tel: 01779 472663 Fax: 01779 478989

RIES WOOLS
Ries Wools. 242-243 High Holborn, London WC1V 7DZ

RIVERSIDE SPINNING
Yarn spinners specialising in yarns for the home machine knitter both wholesale and retail. Acrylic wool blends, space dyed yarns with lurex. Mail order available.
Riverside Spinning. Dock Mill, Dockfield Terrace, Shipley, West Yorkshire BD17 7AW
Tel; 01274 596875

RKM WOOLS / YARNWORKS MAIL ORDER
36-39 Chester Street, Wrexham LL13 8AH
Tel: 01978 266262

ROWAN YARNS

A beautiful range of designer yarns in a wide range shades. Aran, Lambswool, D.K and chunky tweeds, botany, cotton chenille, cotton glace, mercerised cotton, cotton and silk mixes etc.

Rowan Yarns. Green Lane Mill, Holmfirth, West Yorkshire HD7 1RW
Tel: 01484 681881 Fax: 01484 687920

SHADES OF CASHMERE

Specialist business selling 100% cashmere, cashmere blends and luxury yarns for the domestic machine knitter and hand knitter. Patterns and kits available.

Shades of Cashmere. Grove Farm, Wolvey, Hinckley, Leicestershire LE10 3LL
Tel/Fax: 01455 220767

SHILASDAIR, THE SKYE YARN COMPANY

Natural dyed and self-coloured yarn, spun from Scottish Gotland and Shetland fleece. Handknitted garments - adult and childrens and knit kits. Mail order.

Shilasdair, The Skye Yarn Company. Waternish, Isle of Skye, Scotland IV55 8GL
Tel: 01470 592 297

SILKSTONE

Quality handknitting yarns - Filatura di Crosa, Colinette, Cashmere, Alpaca, Silk etc. Services directory, yarns, books, training and workshops. Retail outlet and mail order.

Silkstone. 12 Market Place, Cockermouth, Cumbria CA13 9NQ
Tel: 01900 821052 Fax: 01900 821051

SILVERKNIT YARNS

Cotton, viscose, lurex, acrylics, yarns on cone.

Silverknit Yarns. Park Road, Calverton, Nottingham NG14 6LL

SIMPLY SHETLAND

Mail order business supplying coned yarn for home and trade customers: 4ply Shetland, Shetland/silk knopp, lambswool, lambswool/silk knopp, lambswool boucle, 2ply merino, cotton and Aran. Large range of colours of Shetland Yarns.

Simply Shetland. Unit 11, Fisherron Industrial Estate, Newhailles Road, Musselburgh, Scotland EH21 6RU
Tel/Fax: 0131 665 6711

SIRDAR PLC

Yarns and designs for handknitting. Specialities include: plain and fancy knit yarns for handknitting, some for machine knitting, Snowflake Fleece Look Fashion, pure cotton and Woolrich yarns available from Sirdar stockists nationwide.

Sirdar PLC. Flanshaw Lane, Alverthorpe, Wakefield, West Yorkshire WF2 9ND
Tel: 01924 371501 Fax: 01924 290506

SOLO YARNS

Alafoss Lopi available.

Solo Yarns. Solo House, Seaham Grange Industrial Estate, Seaham, Co. Durham SR7 0PW

SPECTRUM YARNS LTD

Produce woollen, worsted and fancy yarns using both natural and synthetic fibres for the knitwear, weaving, knitting and upholstery industry.

Spectrum Yarns Ltd. Spa Mills, New Street, Slaithwaite, Huddersfield HD7 5BB
Tel: 01484 843732 Fax: 01484 847784

SPINNERS

Naturally dyed specialist in hand dyed yarns.

Spinners
Tel: 0201 8692 2958 Fax: 020 8673 2760

SPINRITE

Canadian yarn in pure new machine washable merino wool and 100% cotton. Double knitting to bulky weights. Suitable for both hand and machine knitting use.

Spinrite. 11 Iliffe House, Iliffe Avenue, Oadby, Leicester LE16 7UP
Tel: 0116 271 0077 Fax: 0116 271 0099

SPRINGWOOLS LTD

Discount retail and wholesale wool shop and stockists of Twilleys, Rowan, Kicarra, Yeoman, Copely and Marshall, Robin etc. Also designer yarns and yarns produced to order.

Springwools Ltd. Old Sawmills, Ballymount Road, Dublin 12, Ireland
Tel: 00 353 1 4509134 Fax: 00 353 1 4509233

STYLECRAFTS

PO Box 62 Goulbourne Street, Keighley, West Yorkshire BD21 1PP
Tel: 01535 609798 Fax: 01535 669952

TEXERE YARNS

Wool, silk, glitter, mohair, cotton, acrylic, ribbon and fancy yarns for hand and machine knitting, tassel work, braid making, weaving and embroidery. Personal visitors are welcome. Mail order available.

Texere Yarns. College Mills, Barkerend Road, Bradford BD3 9AQ
Tel: 01274 722191 Fax: 01274 393500

THOMAS B. RAMSDEN & CO. LTD

Handknitting yarns.

Thomas B. Ramsden & Co. Ltd. Netherfield Road, Guiseley, West Yorkshire LS20 9PD
Tel: 01943 872264

TIVOLI SPINNERS LTD

Knitting yarns and designs.

Tivoli Spinners Ltd. Unit 3, Shorade Industrial Estate, New Street, Bridgtown, Cannock, Staffordshire WS11 3DD
Tel: 01543 467080/467081 Fax: 01543 467091

TWENTY-FIRST CENTURY YARNS

Exclusive hand dyed natural yarns. Mail order.

Twent-First Century Yarns. Unit 14, Earl Soham Lodge, Earl Soham, Suffolk IP13 7SA
Tel: 01394 387659

TWILLEYS OF STAMFORD

Hand dyed yarns and threads in a wide range of colours and textures, in natural fibres for all creative textile arts. Mail order and exhibitions only.

Twilleys of Stamford. Roman Mill, Stamford, Lincolnshire PE9 1BG
Tel: 01780 752661 Fax: 01780 765215

TYNSELL HANDSPINNING SUPPLIES

Handspinning equipment, wool for spinning, felting and all natural fibres, American magazines, wider ranging book list. Mail order only.

Tynsell Handspinning Supplies. 53 Cross Green Road, Huddersfield HD5 9XX
Tel: 01484 534273 Fax: 01484 518328

UNDY YARNCRAFTS

Suppliers of yarns and accessories for machine knitting, weaving, spinning, dyeing and crochet etc. Representatives of the British Angora Producers' Marketing Association. Suppliers of angora fibre and yarn, grown, processed and spun in Britain.

Undy Yarncrafts. The Old Temperance Hall, West End, Magor, Monmouthshire NP6 3HT
Tel: 01633 881183 Fax: 01633 881028

UPPINGHAM YARNS LTD

Full range of yarns for machine and handknitting at excellent prices, supplying designers, students, home knitters, knitwear retailers and to the trade. Yarn warehouse: acrylics, cotton, wool and wool blends, lambswool, boucle, cashmere, crepe, chenille, mohair, many fancies, silk, linen mixes, lurex and specialist yarns.

Uppingham Yarns Ltd. 22 North Street East, Uppingham, Rutland LE15 9QL
Tel: 01572 823747

VICTORIA FLOYD - HANDYED TEXTILES

A unique collection of hand-dyed threads, yarns and hand worked papers. Please contact for sales tables and mail order details. Yarns: viscose, cotton, rayon, cotton slubs, cotton acrylics, linen, viscose, chenille, space and flat dyed yarns.

Victoria Floyd. 5 Field End, Stourport-on-Severn, Worcestershire PY13 8UD
Tel: 01299 823875

WEAVERKNITS LTD

Coned yarns from 1ply through to double knit. Machine spares, knitting and sewing machines. 5ply Guernsey wool on cone in navy and natural colours.

Weaverknits Ltd. 276-278 Main Road, Sutton-at-Hone, Nr. Dartford, Kent DA4 9HJ
Tel: 01322 863144 Fax: 01322 862472

WEBBS GREEN FARM WOOL

Jacob, Manx, Loghtan and Corriedale wool produced and available for sale on the farm for handspinning, handknitting and handweaving. By appointment or by mail order.

Webbs Green Farm Wool. Webbs Green Farm, Soberton, Southampton, Hampshire SO32 3PY
Tel: 01489 877465

THE WENSLEYDALE LONGWOOL SHEEPSHOP

Commission spinners and dyers ranges of Aran, double knit, 4ply, 2ply, hand and machine knitting yarns from the soft and lustrous fleece of rare Wensleydale sheep, knitting kits and patterns also available. Trade and Mail order available or visit the shop Tues-Sat, April to October or by appointment.

The Wensleydale Longwool Sheepshop. Cross Lanes Farm, Garriston, Leyburn, North Yorkshire DL8 5JU
Tel/Fax: 01969 623840

WILLIAM WHITE & SONS

Mercerised cotton, silk, rayon, synthetics and many fancy yarns.

William White & Sons. Wilspur Mills, New Mill, Huddersfield HD7 7ET
Tel: 01484 682306 Fax: 01484 684970

WOOL 2 EWE

Knitting wool, accessories, patterns, books and haberdashery, by mail order.

Wool 2 Ewe. "Serica" 40 Tolworth Road, Surbiton, Surrey KT6 7SZ

WOOLWORKS

Ethnic yarns, Lopi, Guernsey, Pure Wool and Arans.

Woolworks. 180 Park View, Whitley Bay North, Tyneside

THE WOOL WORKSHOP

Cornish wools, Arans, handyed wools to your own colours and shades, fleeces to spin.

The Wool Workshop. Tremorvah Padstow, Cornwall PL28 8LE
Tel: 01841 533046

WORTH KNITTING

Machine and handknitting yarns. Large range of coned yarns. Large mail order range. Warehouse open to the public. Visitors welcome.

Worth Knitting. Wesley Road, Armley, Leeds LS12 1UH
Tel: 0113 279 8858 Fax: 0113 279 8853

YARNARAMA

Industrial yarns, knitting and sewing machines, overlockers and accessories.

Yarnarama. BSK Ltd. Murdock Road, Manton Industrial Estate, Bedford MK41 7LE
Tel: 01234 217096 Fax: 01234 271537

YEOMAN YARNS LTD

Industrial knitting and weaving yarn suppliers in mainly synthetic/natural blends in all fibres. Dyed and undyed: cotton, fancy and classic for knitwear and jersey markets.

Yeoman Yarns Ltd. 36 Churchill Way, Fleckney, Leicestershire LE8 8UD
Tel: 01162 404464 Fax: 0116 402522

YORKSHIRE MOHAIR MILLS

Yorkshire Mohair Mills. Gibson Street, Bradford BD3 9TS
Tel: 01274 668686

ASSOCIATION OF APPLIED ARTS

6 Darnaway Street, Edinburgh EH3 6BG
Tel: 0131 220 5070 Fax: 0131 225 5660

ASSOCIATION OF CREATIVE CRAFTS & ART

ACCA Administration Centre. PO Box 41, Driffield, East Yorkshire Y025 8YX
Tel: 01377 253900 Fax: 01377 255918

ASSOCIATION OF ILLUSTRATORS

First Floor, 32-38 Saffron Hill, London EC1N 8FH
Tel: 020 7831 7377

ASSOCIATION OF MASTER UPHOLSTERERS & FURNISHERS

Frances Vaughan House, 102 Commercial Street, Newport, Gwent NP9 1LU
Tel: 01633 215454 Fax: 01633 244488

ASSOCIATION OF MODEL AGENTS

122 Brompton Road, London SW3 1JE
Tel: 020 7584 6466

ART WORKERS' GUILD

6 Queen Square, London WC1N 3AR
Tel: 020 7837 3474

THE ASSOCIATION OF GUILDS OF WEAVERS, SPINNERS & DYERS

Founded in 1955, the association has 102 affiliated UK guilds, plus 9 overseas, to promote and maintain excellence of craftsmanship, the exchange of information and develop the aims of the individual through achievement. British agents register.

The Association of Guilds of Weavers, Spinners & Dyers. 2 Bower Mount Road, Maidstone, Kent ME16 8AU
Tel: 01622 678429

ASSOCIATION OF RAG RUG MAKERS

1 Wingrad House, Jubilee Street, London E1 3BJ
Tel: 020 7790 1093

BEAD SOCIETY OF GREAT BRITAIN

Ventira, Horseshoe Road, Spalding, Lincolnshire PE11 3BE

THE BEAD STUDY TRUST

Charitable trust promoting research into all aspects of beads, their history and use. Publishes a newsletter twice a year. Administers the Guilds scholarship fund.

The Bead Study Trust. 29 Elliscombe Road, Charlton, London SE7 7PF
Tel: 0181 858 2649

BRITISH AGENTS REGISTER

24 Mount Parade, Harrogate, North Yorkshire HG1 1BP
Tel: 01423 560608 Fax: 01423 561204

BRITISH BUTTON MANUFACTURERS' ASSOCIATION

21 Cole Park Road, Twickenham, Middlesex TW1 1HP
Tel: 020 8891 1253 Fax: 020 8892 4797

THE BRITISH BUTTON SOCIETY

The British Button Society promotes the study and collection of buttons: uniform, fashion and costume. The society conducts research providing information through membership and their quarterly journal: Button Lines.

The British Button Society. The old Diary, Newton, Kettering, Northamptonshire NN15 1BW
Tel: 01536 461818 Fax: 01536 561818

BRITISH CLOTHING INDUSTRIES ASSOCIATION LTD

5 Portland Place, London W1N 3AA
Tel: 020 7636 7515

BRITISH DISPLAY SOCIETY

The independent professional body for visual merchandising, display, point of sale, exhibition, design and training.

British Display Society. 146 Welling Way, Welling, Kent DA16 2RS
Tel: 020 8856 2030 Fax: 020 8856 9394

BRITISH FASHION COUNCIL

Trade association: fashion, fashion exhibitions and London Fashion Week.

5 Portland Place, London WIN 3AA
Tel: 020 7636 7788 Fax: 020 7636 7515

BRITISH FOOTWEAR ASSOCIATION

5 Portland Place, London W1N 3AA
Tel: 020 7580 8687 Fax: 020 7580 8986

BRITISH GLOVE ASSOCIATION (formerly the Glove Guild)

The British Glove Association is a glove promoting body, formerly the Glove Guild of Great Britain. Its purpose is to promote gloves by all means available. Annual Glove Design competition.

British Glove Association. Crane & Partners, Rutland House,
44 Masons Hill Bromley, Kent BR2 9EG
Tel: 020 8464 0131 Fax: 020 8464 6018

BRITISH HANDKNITTING CONFEDERATION LTD

Nappa House, Scott Lane, Riddlesden, Keighley, West Yorkshire BD20 5BU
Tel: 01535 603450

BRITISH HAT GUILD

Trade association - information available on sources of supply and millinery training.

The British Hat Guild. The Business Centre, Kimpton Road, Luton LU2 0LB
Tel: 0845 357 0357 Fax: 01582 705088

BRITISH INSTITUTE OF INTERIOR DESIGN

1C, Devonshire Avenue, Beeston, Nottingham NG9 1BS

BRITISH INTERIOR TEXTILES' ASSOCIATION

Association relating to the furnishing textiles industry, manufacture and distribution.

**British Interior Textiles Association. Reedham House, 31 King Street,
West Manchester M3 2PF**
Tel: 020 7636 7788 Fax: 020 636 7515

BRITISH KNITTING & CLOTHING CONFEDERATION

5 Portland Place, London W1N 3AA
Tel: 020 7636 7788 Fax: 020 7636 7515

BRITISH KNITTING & CLOTHING EXPORTS COUNCIL

Trade association promoting exports from the UK of all apparel and fashion accessories.
Associate members include suppliers to the clothing trade.

British Knitting & Clothing Exports Council. 5 Portland Place, London WIN 3AA
Tel: 020 7636 7788 Fax: 020 7636 7515

BLC. LEATHER TECHNOLOGY CENTRE

A specialist in leather technology offering a wide range of technical services, including routine
testing, comprehensive problem solving, training, consultancy and research.

**BLC. Leather Technology Centre. Leather Trade House, Kings Park Road,
Moulton Park, Northampton NN3 6JD**
Tel: 01604 679999 Fax: 01604 679998

BRITISH LEATHER FASHION COUNCIL

International fashion colour forecasting service.

**British Leather Fashion Council, Leather Trade House, King's Park Road, Moulton Park,
Northampton NN3 6JD**
Tel: 01604 67999 Fax: 01604 679998

BRITISH MENSWEAR GUILD LTD

The British Menswear Guild Ltd. is an export sales and marketing led trade association of
manufacturers of high quality branded menswear. The Guild activities are focused on export
promotion, representing Britain's finest branded mens clothing and accessory manufacturers.

The British Menswear Guild. 1 Saville Row, London W1X 2JR
Tel: 020 7734 6211 Fax: 020 7734 6277

BRITISH NARROW FABRICS ASSOCIATION

Trade association.

British Narrow Fabrics Association. Thorncliffe, 115 Windsor Road, Oldham, OL8 1RQ
Tel: 0161 620 7272 Fax: 0161 620 7273

BRITISH NEEDLECRAFTS COUNCIL

143 Queens Road, Halifax, West Yorkshire HX1 4LN
Tel: 01422 320642

BRITISH TEXTILE MACHINERY ASSOCIATION

20 Ralli Courts, West Riverside, Manchester M3 5FL
Tel: 0161 834 2991 Fax: 0161 834 2991

BRITISH TEXTILE TECHNOLOGY GROUP (BTTG)

Independent textile research and consultancy centre, concerned principally with all scientific aspects of textile production, specification and performance. Also concerned with the testing, investigation, training services and evaluation at all stages of production and use. Training services.

British Textile Technology Group. (BTTG) Wira House, West Park Ring Road, Leeds LS16 6QL
Tel: 0113 259 1999 Fax: 0113 278 0306

BRITISH WOOL MARKETING BOARD

Oak Mills, Station Road, Clayton, Bradford, West Yorkshire BD14 6JD
Tel: 01274 882091 Fax: 01274 737549

THE BUSINESS DESIGN CENTRE

52 Upper Street, Islington, London N1 0QH
Tel: 020 7359 3535 www.newdesigners.com

THE BUTTONHOOK SOCIETY

A collectors society to encourage the research, collection and preservation of buttonhooks and accessories. Archives and 50,000 + buttonholes. Research into their history, origins and manufacture. Meetings and exhibitions, books and lectures.

The Buttonhook Society. 2 Romney Place, Maidstone, Kent ME15 6LE
Tel/Fax: 01622 752949

CAPIT B

The national training organisation for the British Apparel and Leather Good Industries. Responsible for vocational education, training and qualifications.

CAPIT B. 80 Richardshaw Lane, Pudsey, Leeds LS28 6BN
Tel: 0113 227 3345 Fax: 0113 227 3322

CENTRAL COUNCIL FOR THE IRISH LINEN INDUSTRY LTD

First Floor, 5C The Square, Hillsborough, Co. Down BT26 6AG
Tel: 01846 689999

CHARLES RENNIE MACKINTOSH SOCIETY

870 Garscube Road, Glasgow
Tel: 0141 946 6600

CHARTERED SOCIETY OF DESIGNERS - CSD

Professional body representing fashion and textile designers, offering chartered staus, membership services, benefits career advice and training. Student membership available for those studying on recognised design courses.

Chartered Society of Designers - CSD. 32-38 Saffron Hill, London EC1N 8SG
Tel: 020 7831 9777 Fax: 020 7831 6277

THE CLOTHING CENTRE

Resource centre providing a design and pattern cutting bureau service. Also a wide range of training iniatives on offer.

The Clothing Centre. Enterprise House, Courtaulds Way, Coventry CV6 5NX
Tel: 01203 637025 Fax: 01203 638796

THE CLOTHING & FOOTWEAR INSTITUTE

Now part of the Textile Institute. Offers various levels of membership for those concerned with production or marketing of clothing and footwear.

The Clothing & Footwear Institute - (see entry for The Textile Institute)

THE CLOTHING TECHNOLOGY CENTRE

SATRA House, Rockingham Road, Kettering, Northants NN16 9JH
Tel: 01536 410000 Fax: 01536 410626

COMPUTER TEXTILE DESIGN GROUP

The Computer Textile Design Group welcomes textile-minded members who wish to share their computer skills, knowledge and enthusiasm with like minded people.
Promotion and use of graphics in textile work: embroidery, surface design, knitting, lace making, screen printing, beading, fashion and many other related areas. Quarterly newsletter features software reviews and using techniques.

Computer Textile Design Group. Galleybirds, Fielden Road, Crowborough, East Sussex TN6 1TP
Tel: 01892 669030

CONFEDERATION OF BRITISH WOOL TEXTILES LTD

Merrydale House, Roydsdale Way, Bradford, West Yorkshire BD4 6SB
Tel: 01274 652207 Fax: 01274 682293

THE COSTUME AND TEXTILE ASSOCIATION FOR NORFOLK MUSEUMS

Carrow house, 301 King Street, Norwich NR1 2TG

THE COSTUME & TEXTILE SOCIETY OF WALES

C/O Museum of Welsh Life, St. Fagans, Cardiff CF5 6XB
Tel: 01222 573500 Fax: 01222 573490

THE COSTUME & TEXTILE STUDY CENTRE

Access to museum collections and library facilities for researchers, available Tuesday and Thursdays.

The Costume & Textile Study Centre. Carrow House, 301 King Street, Norwich NR1 2TS
Tel: 01603 223870

COTTON TECHNOLOGY INTERNATIONAL

Dale House, 204 London Road, Hazel Grove, Stockport SK7 4DF
Tel: 0161 483 8121 Fax: 0161 483 8144

CRAFTS COUNCIL

The national centre for crafts, housing an exhibition gallery, reference and picture libraries, the crafts council, gallery and shops.

The Crafts Council. 44A Pentonville Road, Islington, London N1 9BY
Tel: 020 7278 7700 Fax: 020 7837 6891

THE CRAFTS GUILD

2 Bathwick Terrace, Bath BA2 4EL
Tel: 01225 461821

CREATIVE INDUSTRIES ASSOCIATION

To promote and give the industry a higher profile, to offer help and advice to both new and established businesses.

Creative Industries Association. PO Box 2238, Christchurch BH23 5YR
Tel: 01425 272711 Fax: 01425 279369

CROSS STITCH GUILD

Pinks Barn, London Road, Fairford GL7 4AR
Tel: 0800 328 9750

THE DESIGN COUNCIL

34 Bow Street,London WC2E 7DL
Tel: 020 7420 5200 Fax: 020 7420 5300

DESIGN NATION

Design Nation is the wholly-owned subsidary of The Design Trust. Design-Nation assists talented new designers in achieving commercial aims.

Design Nation. 9 Burgess Hill, London NW2 2BY
Tel: 020 7431 6329 Fax: 020 7435 5487

THE DESIGN & TECHNOLOGY ASSOCIATION

Professional association representing those involved in design and technology education. Runs conferences and courses, publishes widely including Designing, A3 magazine providing teachers and pupils with information, inspiration and classroom display materials.

The Design & Technology Association. 16 Wellesbourne House, Walton Road, Wellesbourne, Warwickshire CV35 9JB
Tel: 01789 470007 Fax: 01789 841955

DESIGN TRUST

A membership based organisation for new graduate designers and design companies, providing a unique, personal support network to British Designers.

Design Trust. 9 Burgess Hill, London NW2 2BY
Tel: 020 7431 6329 Fax: 020 7435 5487

DESIGN WORKERS GUILD

The Porch House, Swan Hill, Shrewsbury SY1 1NQ
Tel: 01743 241031

EMBROIDERERS' GUILD

The Embroiderers' Guild is an educational charity with 200 branches nationwide, housing the museum collection, library and extensive bookshop. It offers a workshop programme including INSET days. Historical and contemporary exhibition. Book and gift catalogue available.

Embroiderer's Guild. Apartment 41, Hampton Court Palace, East Molesley, Surrey KT8 9AU
Tel: 020 8943 1229 Fax: 020 8977 9882

EUROPEAN TEXTILE NETWORK

Set up to promote European co-operation and cultural interchanges in textiles.

ETN Secretariat, PO Box 5944, D-30059, Hanover, Germany.

THE FABRIC CARE RESEARCH ASSOCIATION LTD (FCRA)

Laundering and dry cleaning technology centre, textile testing, specialists in garment care and labelling. Project work undertaken. Membership discounts.

The Fabric Care Research Association Ltd (FCRA). Forest House Laboratories, Knaresborough Road, Harrogate, North Yorkshire HG2 7LZ
Tel: 01423 885977 Fax: 01423 880045

FEDERATION OF BRITISH ARTISTS

17 Carlton House Terrace, London SW1Y 5BD
Tel: 020 7930 6844

FAN CIRCLE INTERNATIONAL

106 Earls Court Road, London W8 6EG
Tel: 020 7937 4916

FASHION & TEXTILE EDUCATIONAL CONSULTANCY

Promotes and supports the development of Fashion & Textiles in Education.

FATEC. Fashion & Textile Educational Consultancy. PO Box 26, Boston, Lincolnshire PE21 9BL
Tel/Fax: 01205 355360

FIFE CRAFT ASSOCIATION

Founded in 1986 to promote craft activities and to encourage the exchange of ideas and experiences.

Fife Craft Association. 12 Valley Grove, Leslie, Glenrothes, Fife KY6 3BZ
Tel: 01592 743539

THE FINE CRAFTS GUILD

Association of designer craftsmakers in business, providing marketing and business opportunities helping members to reach new markets and increase income.

The Fine Crafts Guild. 61 Old London Road, Hastings, East Sussex TN35 5NB
Tel: 01424 436565 Fax: 01424 437003

Embroiderers' Guild

sharing opportunities for discovery and creativity

Join the Embroiderers' Guild – help us to protect and develop our rich heritage of embroidery. Membership to the Embroiderers' Guild is the key to unlocking the door to a world of stitches, colours and textures.

Apartment 41, Hampton Court Palace, Surrey KT8 9AU
Tel: +44 (0)20 8943 1229
Fax: +44 (0)20 8977 9882
email: administrator@embroiderersguild.org.uk
www. embroiderersguild.org.uk

Embroiders' Guild Registered Charity No. 234239
Registered Museum with the Museum Galleries Commission

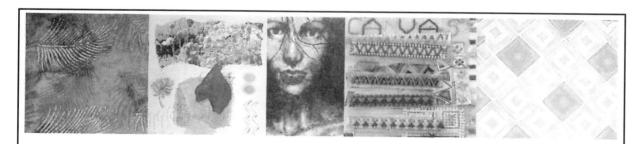

Young Embroiderers

for young members of the Embroiderers' Guild between 5 and 18 years of age

Young Embroiderers receive the Textile Ideas magazine three times a year which is full of projects and activities.
There are over 90 Young Embroiderers groups throughout the country for members to join if they wish.
As well as the Young Embroiderers web site, there are numerous competitions and events for members to join in with.

Join today

Young Embroiderers
Apartment 41, Hampton Court Palace, Surrey KT8 9AU
Tel: +44 (0)20 8943 1229
Fax: +44 (0)20 8977 9882
email: administrator@embroiderersguild.org.uk
www. embroiderersguild.org.uk/youngembroiderers/

GROUP FOR COSTUME & TEXTILE STAFF IN MUSEUMS

State Apartments & Court Dress Collection, Kensington Palace, London W8 4PX

GUILD OF DISABLED HOMEWORKERS

Market Street, Nailsworth, Gloucestershire GL6 0BX

GUILD OF MACHINE KNITTERS

Charitable organisation devoted to supporting and raising standards of machine knitting. The Guild consists of designers, manufacturers, educators and other interested people. Publishes a quarterly newsletter.

Guild of Machine Knitters. 48 Littlepark Avenue, Bedhampton, Havant, Hampshire P09 3QY
Tel: 01705 475251

THE GUILD OF NEEDLELACES

72 Hawes Close, Northwood, Middlesex HA6 1EW
Tel: 01923 829844

GUILD OF TRADITIONAL UPHOLSTERERS

Founded in 1987 the Guild exists to uphold standards of excellence in and to promote the craft of traditional handmade upholstery.

Guild of Traditional Upholsterers. Loosehanger Park, Redlynch, Salisbury, Wiltshire SP5 2PS
Tel: 01794 388892

HARRIS TWEED AUTHORITY

Provides leaflets, brochures and videos - available for loan.

Harris Tweed Authority. 6 Garden Road, Stornoway, Isle of Lewis
Tel: 01851 702269 Fax: 01851 702600

HAT PIN SOCIETY OF GREAT BRITAIN

To promote the collecting of hat pins and hat pin holders.

PO Box 74, Bozeat, Northants NN29 7JH

HINCKLEY & DISTRICT KNITTING ASSOCIATION

Employers association for knitting companies in the Hinckley area.

Hinckley & District Knitting Association. 37 Station Road, Hinckley, Leicestershire LE10 1AP
Tel: 01455 238771 Fax: 01455 238205

HISTORIC NEEDLEWORK GUILD

Hanging by Thread. PO Box 10723, London SE3 OZL

INTERNATIONAL APPAREL FEDERATION

As the sole representative for apparel manufactures worldwide, it provides a unique link for both manufacturers and other apparel related companies in terms of creating business links, supporting development in technology, education and training.

International Apparel Federation. 5 Portland Place, London W1H 3AA
Tel: 020 7636 7788 Fax: 020 7436 8261

INTERNATIONAL FASHION FEDERATION

55 Conduit Street, London W1R 9FD
Tel: 020 7434 1994 Fax: 020 7287 2443

INTERNATIONAL SEWING MACHINE COLLECTORS' SOCIETY

48 Nightingale House, Thomas More Street, London E1 9UB
Tel: 020 7488 0474 Fax: 020 7481 9097

INTERNATIONAL MOHAIR ASSOCIATION

Mohair House, 68 The Grove, Ilkley, West Yorkshire LS29 9PA
Tel: 01943 817149

INTERNATIONAL WOOL SECRETARIATE

2nd Floor, 40 New Bond Street, London W1Y 9FD
Tel: 020 7499 1555 Fax: 020 7499 0666

IRISH LINEN GUILD

Promotion organisation for the Irish Linen Industry, providing information on Irish Linen.

Irish Linen Guild. 5C The Square, Hillsborough, Ireland BT26 6AG
Tel: 01846 689999 Fax: 01846 689968

THE KNITTING CRAFT GROUP

The Knitting Craft Group seeks to motivate parents and teachers to encourage the next generation to enjoy handknitting, machine knitting and crochet. Educational and inspirational resources for handknitting and crochet (project leaflets, wallcharts, slide sets - 35mm colour, with lecture notes). Send SAE for price list and details.

The Knitting Craft Group. Alba, Cwmfelin Mynach, Whitland,
Dyfed, South Wales SA34 0DH
Tel: 01994 448430

THE KNITTING AND CROCHET GUILD

A leading national organisation for the promotion of knitting and crochet. An educational charity preserving the practice, preservation, development and continuance of the skills, raising of standards and promotion of knitting and crochet. Mail order for all resources.

The Knitting & Crochet Guild.
228 Chester Road North, Kidderminster, Worcestershire DY10 1TH
Tel: 01562 754367

THE KNITTING INDUSTRIES FEDERATION LTD

Promotion of UK Knitting Industries organisation, including goverment national trade lobbying, comprehensive industrial relations versus health and safety services, together with environmental issues and statistics.

The Knitting Industries Federation Ltd. 53 Oxford Street, Leicester LE1 5XY
Tel: 0116 254 1608 Fax: 0116 254 2273

THE KNITTING AND LACE INDUSTRIES

Training Resource Centre, Agency 7, Gregory Boulevard, Nottingham NG7 6LD

LACE GUILD

To promote the study, collecting and use of lace.

The Lace Guild. The Hollies, 53 Audnam, Stourbridge, West Midlands DY8 4AE
Tel: 01384 390739 Fax: 01384 444415

LACE SOCIETY

To further the making and collecting of handmade lace including pillow lace.

**The Lace Society. Lynwood, Stratford Road, Oversley Green, Alcester,
Warwickshire B49 6PG**

THE LEATHER PRODUCERS' ASSOCIATION

Leather Trade House, Kings Park Road, Moulton Park, Northampton NN3 6JD
Tel: 01604 494131

LEICESTER & DISTRICT KNITTING INDUSTRY ASSOCIATION LTD

53 Oxford Street, Leicester
Tel: 0116 254 1608

LIVERPOOL COTTON ASSOCIATION

620 Cotton Exchange Buildings, Edmund Street, Liverpool L3 9LH
Tel: 0151 236 6041 Fax: 0151 255 0174

NADCAT
NOTTINGHAM & DERBYSHIRE CLOTHING & TEXTILES ASSOCIATION LTD

Ashfield Business Centre, The Idlwells, Sutton in Ashfield, Nottinghamshire NG17 1BL
Tel: 01623 440612 Fax: 01623 442102

NATIONAL ASSOCIATION OF DISABLED CRAFT WORKERS

Piethorn Cottage, Barrachan by Mochrum, Newtown Stewart, Wigtownshire DG8 9NF
Tel: 01988 860204

NATIONAL ASSOCIATION FOR EDUCATION IN ART & DESIGN

7A The High Street, Corsham, Wiltshire SP1 3TP

NATIONAL ASSOCIATION OF TEACHERS OF
HOME ECONOMICS & TECHNOLOGY

Provides subject support for textile technology teachers.
Membership and a wide selection of resources available.

National Association of Teachers of Home Economics. Hamilton House,
Mabledon Place, London WC1H 9BJ
Tel: 020 7387 1441 Fax: 020 7383 7230

NATIONAL PATCHWORK ASSOCIATION

Membership association for patchwork, quilting and embroidery. Quarterly newsletter and exhibitions.

National Patchwork Association. PO Box 300, Hethersett, Norwich, Norfolk NR9 3DH
Tel: 01603 812259

NATIONAL TEXTILE TRAINING GROUP

Jarodale House, 7 Gregory Boulevard, Nottingham NG7 6LD
Tel: 01159 531866

THE NEEDLELOOM FELT MANUFACTURERS ASSOCIATION

3 Manchester Road, Bury, Lancashire BL9 0DR

NEW DESIGNERS EXHIBITION

New Designers is the annual national showcase of over 2000 British and Irish graduating
designers from fashion, textile and accessory design.

New Designers Exhibition. 52 Upper Street, Islington, London N1 0QH
Tel: 020 7359 3535 Fax: 020 7288 6446

NORTHERN IRELAND TEXTILE & APPAREL ASSOCIATION

Trade association for the Textile and Clothing Industry.

Northern Ireland Textiles & Apparel Association. 5C The Square,
Hillsborough, Co. Down B126 6AG
Tel: 01846 689999 Fax: 01846 689968

NORWICH CATHEDRAL BRODERER'S GUILD

Design and provision of new altar frontals and vestments. Restoration and repairs and alterations to existing ecclesiastical work. Advice and referral for conservation. Repair, restoration of Ecclesiastical vestments and altar frontals. New work undertaken

**Norwich Cathedral Broderer's Guild. Norwich Cathedaral,
12 The Close, Norwich Norfolk NR1 4DH**
Tel: 01603 764838 Fax: 01603 766032

NOTTINGHAM FASHION CENTRE

Huntingdon Street, Nottingham NG1 3lH
Tel: 0115 9153800 Fax 0115 9153805

THE PLASTICS AND RUBBER ADVISORY SERVICE

6 Bath Place, Rivington Street, London EC2A 3JE
Tel: 0991 908070 Fax: 020 7457 5045

QUALIFICATIONS FOR INDUSTRY LTD

The awarding body for National/Scottish Vocational Qualifications, including: manufacturing sewn products, customer service, key skills, manufacturing textiles and handcraft tailoring.

Qualifications for Industry Ltd. 80 Richardshaw Lane, Pudsey, Leeds LS28 6BN
Tel: 0113 227 3300 Fax: 0113 227 3001

THE QUILTER'S GUILD OF THE BRITISH ISLES

The Quilter's Guild of the British Isles is open to anyone interested in the contemporary or traditional quiltmaking worlds.

**The Quilter's Guild of the British Isles. Room 190, Dean Clough,
Halifax, West Yorkshire HX3 5AX**
Tel: 01422 347669 Fax: 01422 345017

REAL SHEEPSKIN ASSOCIATION

The Real Sheepskin Association represents sheepskin tanners, manufacturers, merchants, retailers, after carers and designers specialising in real sheepskin products. Sponsors of the "Real Sheepskin Design Award" - Graduate Fashion Week - The Real Sheepskin Category.

Real Sheepskin Association. 60 Main Road, Hackleton, Northampton NN7 2AB
Tel: 01604 870703 Fax: 01604 870430

REGISTER OF APPAREL & TEXTILE DESIGNERS

The register offers a help and advice service to freelance designers and also acts as a design studio, puting manufacturers and retailers in touch with designers. Holds lists of practising freelance designers to assist British manufacturers of the Clothing and Textile Indusy.

**Register of Apparel & Textile Designers. British Apparel Centre,
7 Swallow Place, London W1N 3AA**
Tel: 020 7636 7788 Fax: 020 7636 7515

ROYAL SOCIETY FOR THE ENCOURAGEMENT OF ARTS, MANUFACTURERS & COMMERCE

Administers the RSA student design awards.

Royal Society of Arts. 8 John Adam Street, London WC2N 6EZ
Tel: 020 7930 5115

THE SCOTTISH BORDERS STUDIO - SCOTTISH ENTERPRISES LTD

Bridge Street, Galashiels TD1 1SW
Tel: 01750 23211/20900 Fax: 01750 22395

SCOTTISH TARTANS' SOCIETY

Reference and design service, keepers of the register of all publicly known Tartans-name and Tartan reports. Archive library and reference service to study and record the origins and development of Tartans and highland dress. Running of two museums - Edinburgh, UK and Franklin, North Caroline, USA.

Scottish Tartan Society. Hall of Records, Port-na-Graig Road, Pitlochry,
Perth, Scotland PH16 5ND
Tel: 01796 474079 Fax: 01796 474090

SCOTTISH TEXTILE ASSOCIATION

The Scottish Textile Association has recently been re-constituted to act as a lobbying organisation for the Scottish Textile Industry in Scotland.

The Scottish Textile Association. Heather Mills, South Bridge Street, Selkirk TD7 5DS
Tel: 01750 20211 Fax: 01750 20845

SCOTTISH TEXTILES NETWORK

The Scottish Textiles Network has been formed to act as a central communication point for the Scottish Textiles Industry.

Scottish Textiles Network. 22A Palmerston Place, Edinburgh EH12 5AL
Tel/Fax: 0131 623 6677

SHETLAND KNITWEAR TRADES' ASSOCIATION

Promotion of Shetland Knitwear.

Shetland Knitwear Trades Association. 175A Commercial Street, Lerwick, Shetland ZE1 OHX
Tel: 01595 695631 Fax: 01595 695628

SILK ASSOCIATION OF GREAT BRITAIN

5 Portland Place, London WIN 3AA
Tel: 020 7636 7788 Fax: 020 7636

SILK EDUCATION SERVICE

Information pack and mail order kits of educational materials available from the Silk Association of Great Britain Education Service. Please contact for details.

Working Silk Museum, New Mills, South Street, Braintree, Essex CM7 3GB
Tel: 01376 553393 Fax: 01376 330642

SOCIETY OF DESIGNER CRAFTSMEN LTD

Society for designers - makers that promotes and encourages excellence in professional practice, workmanship, design and to enhance the status of all those who work in the crafts. Licentiateship and membership scheme with opportunities of exhibitions.

Society of Designer Craftsmen Ltd. 24 Rivington Street, London EC2A 3DU
Tel/Fax: 020 7739 3663

SOCIETY OF DYERS & COLOURISTS

The Society is a professional body whose aim is to promote the advancement of the science of colour.

**Society of Dyers & Colourists. Perkin House, PO Box 244,
82 Grattan Road, Bradford BD1 2JB**
Tel: 01274 725138 Fax: 01274 392888

SOCIETY OF SCOTTISH ARTISTS

3A Howe Street, Edinburgh EH3 6TE

SUEDE & LEATHER ADVISORY SERVICE - SUEDE SERVICES LTD

2A Hoop Lane, London NW11 8JS
Tel: 020 8455 0052 Fax: 020 8455 3776

THE TEXTILE CONSERVATION CENTRE

Comprehensive textile conservation service, including advice, treatment and on-site work as well as Postgraduate teaching.

**The Textile Conservation Centre. Apartment 22, Hampton Court Place,
East Moseley, Surrey KT8 9AU**
Tel: 020 8977 4943 Fax: 020 8835 3087

THE TEXTILE INSTITUTE

**International Headquarters, 4th Floor, St. James Buildings,
Oxford Street, Manchester M1 6FQ**
Tel: 0161 237 1188 Fax: 0161 236 1991

THE TEXTILE RESEARCH COUNCIL

Forest House Laboratories, Knaresborough Road, Harrogate, North Yorkshire HG2 7LZ
Tel: 01423 880349 Fax: 01423 880045

THE TEXTILE SOCIETY

A charity which aims to unite scholars, designers, researchers, teachers, artists, collectors and others who share an interest in the study of textile design and history. A society that encourages new research by acting as a medium to the above listed. Meetings, visits and student bursaries available.

The Textile Society. C/O. Walter Bowyer. 173 Brettenham Road, Walthamstow E17 5AX

THE VILENE ORGANISATION
PO Box 3, Greetland, Halifax HX4 8NJ

THE WALLPAPER HISTORY SOCIETY
C/O V & A Museum. South Kensington, London SW7 2RL
Tel: 020 7938 8500

THE WILLIAM MORRIS SOCIETY
Kelmscott House, 26 Upper Mall, Hammersmith, London W6 9TA
Tel: 020 8741 3735

THE WOOLMARK COMPANY
The Woolmark Company is the world's leading textile marketing organisation for wool promotion, technical research, style forecasting, global sourcing, market research, commercial testing and environmental services.

The Woolmark Company. 2nd Floor, 40 New Bond Street, London W1Y 9HB
Tel/Fax: 020 7499 15555

THE WORSHIPFUL COMPANY OF BRODERERS
Livery company.

The Worshipful Company of Broderers. 11 Bridge Road, East Moseley, Surrey KT8 9EU
Tel: 020 8941 3116 Fax: 020 8979 5934

THE YOUNG TEXTILE GROUP
The Young Textile Group is part of the Embroiderers' Guild Association and is open to children & young people under the age of 18 who are interested in working with fabric and threads. There are some 100 groups around the country and memebers receive their own newsletter 3 times a year.

**The Young Textile Group. Apartment 41, Hampton Court Palace,
East Moseley, Surrey KT8 9AU**
Tel: 020 8943 1229 Fax: 020 8977 9882

Remember to mention the
FASHION & TEXTILE INFORMATION DIRECTORY
When ordering your supplies

FATEC
FASHION
AND
TEXTILE
EDUCATIONAL
CONSULTANCY

ABBEY WOOLLEN MILL

Dyeing, blending, carding, spinning, weaving exhibits. Factory shop.

Maritime Industrial Museum. Maritime Quarter, Swansea SA1 1SN
Tel: 01792 650351 Fax: 01792 654200

ABINGTON MUSEUM

19th century Fashion Collection.

Abington Museum, Abington Park, Northampton NN1 5LW
Tel: 01604 631454

ALBY LACE MUSEUM & STUDY CENTRE

Lace exhibits to 300 years old.

**Alby Lace Museum & Study Centre. Alby Craft Centre, Cromer Road,
Alby, Norwich, Norfolk NR11 7QE**
Tel: 01263 768002

ALLHALLOWS MUSEUM

Exhibits include displays of Honiton Lace and other types of lace.
Craft demonstrations through selected months of the year.

Allhallows Museum, High Street, Honiton, Devon EX14 8PE
Tel: 01404 44966

AMERICAN MUSEUM IN BRITAIN

The museum has an extensive collection of North American quilts and other textiles including
Navajo rugs. The library has a collection of specialist related books.

American Museum in Britain. Claverton Manor, Bath BA2 7BD
Tel: 01225 460503 Fax: 01225 480726

BANKFIELD MUSEUM

Bankfield Museum is home to an historical and contemporary collection of international
textiles, costumes and crafts, plus a lively and varied programme of changing exhibitions and
educational activities, including workshops and demonstrations.

Bankfield Museum. Ackroyd Park, Boothtown Road, Halifax, West Yorkshire HX3 6HG
Tel: 01422 354823 or 01422 352334 Fax: 01422 349020

BARNET MUSEUM

Exhibits include samplers and costume along with local artifacts.

Barnet Museum. 31 Wood Street, Barnet, Hertfordshire EN5 4BE
Tel: 020 8440 8066

BECK ISLE MUSEUM OF RURAL LIFE

Museum depicting life over 200 years, specialising in the Victorian period. Twenty seven
gallerys all as rooms, shops, workshops, streets and gents' outfitters.

Beck Isle Museum of Rural Life. Bridge Street, Pickering, North Yorkshire YO18 8DU
Tel: 01751 473653 Fax: 01751 473653

BEXHILL MUSEUM OF COSTUME & SOCIAL HISTORY

Displays include clothes and memorabilia from mid-eighteenth century to modern times, plus special collections of dolls, lace and embroidery.

Bexhill Museum of Costume and Social History. Manor Gardens, Upper Sea Road, Bexhill-on-Sea, East Sussex TN40 1RL
Tel: 01424 210045

BRADFORD INDUSTRIAL MUSEUM

Original Victorian worsted spinning mill, complete with mill owner's house and street of workers' cottages. Textile demonstrations daily.

Bradford Industrial Museum. Moorside Road, Bradford BD2 3HP
Tel: 01274 631756 Fax: 01274 636362

THE CHILDHOOD & COSTUME MUSEUM

The Childhood & Costume Museum. Newmarket Building, Postern Gate, Bridgnorth, Shropshire WV16 4AA
Tel: 01746 764636

COLDHARBOUR MILL WORKING WOOL MUSEUM

Museum of the Devon wool textiles industry located in an 18th century mill. Displays of machinery and artifacts connected with the wool trade. Weaver's cottage, dyers and carpenters workshops. Mill shop sells knitting yarns and garments. New World tapestry on display. Guided tour of the mill.

Coldharbour Mill Working Wool Museum. Coldharbour Mill, Uffculme, Cullompton, Devon EX15 3EE
Tel: 01884 840960 Fax: 01884 840858

THE COLOUR MUSEUM

Award winning museum allowing you to experience the world of colour. (An educational activity of the Society of Dyers and Colourists).

The Colour Museum. Perkin House, PO Box 244, Providence Street, Bradford, West Yorkshire BD1 2PW
Tel: 01274 390955 Fax: 01274 392888

COMMONWEALTH INSTITUTE

Centre for Commonwealth education and culture. Reference library of current Commonwealth literature, art exhibitions and craft shop.

Commonwealth Institute. Kensington High Street, Kensington, London W8
Tel: 020 7603 4535 Fax: 020 7602 7374

THE COSTUME & TEXTILE STUDY CENTRE

Study centre run by Norfolk Museum Service. Formerly housed at Strangers' Hall Museum and moved to carrow House in 1997. The museum houses a comprehensive textile collection and also a costume and accessory collection from seventeen hundred to late twentieth century mens, womens and childrens, with library providing research facilities. Access to the museums collections and library open by appointment on Tuesdays and Thursdays.

The Costume & Textile Study Centre. Carrow House, 301 King Street, Norwich NR1 2TG
Tel: 01603 223870

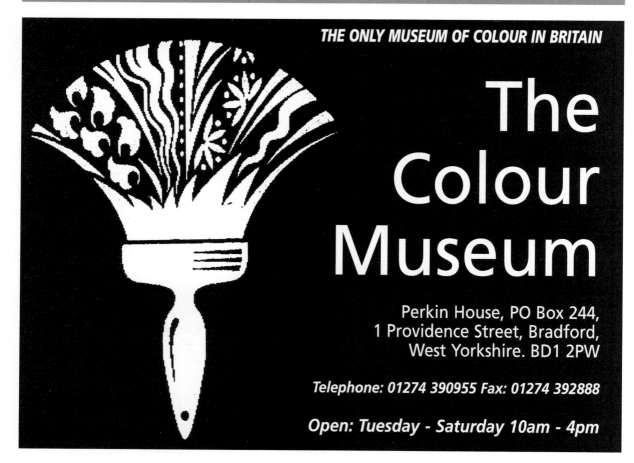

CROMER MUSEUM

Cromer Museum is housed in a row of tiny fishermens cottages besides Cromer Church. The displays tell the story of a Norfolk seaside resort and the landscape around it. The museum exhibits a small collection of Fishermens Ganseys, some on display and a reference section on Ganseys and knitting them.

Cromer Museum. Next to Cromer Parish Church, East Cottages, Tucker Street, Cromer, Norfolk NR27 9HB
Tel: 01263 513543 Fax: 01263 511651

DEAL TOWN HALL EXHIBITION

Collections of costumes, antique dolls and Victoriana.

Deal Town Hall Exhibition. Town Hall, High Street, Deal, Kent CT14 6BB
Tel: 01304 380546

DESIGN MUSEUM

A fascinating introduction to twentieth century design. From cars to cameras, the Design Museum is the first museum of its kind in the world, to look at how design effects our lives. A number of contemporary exhibitions explore in detail the lives of designers, architects and their work.

Design Museum. Butlers Wharf, 28 Shad Thames, London SE1 2YD
Tel: 020 7403 6933 Fax: 020 7378 6540

DUNSTER DOLLS' MUSEUM

Varied collection of over 800 period dolls including a collection of 20 'Sasha' dolls dressed in period costume from 1914 to 1920. Christening robes and dolls house available for viewing.

Dunsters Dolls' Museum. Memorial Hall, High Street, Dunster,
Minehead, Somerset TA24 6SF
Tel: 01643 821220

THE FAN MUSEUM

The fan Museum is the first and only museum in the world dedicated in all its entirety to the ancient art and craft of fans, housed in two beautifully restored, listed Georgian town houses. The museum has study research facilities and a reference library. A wide range of curriculum-based educational programmes is available.

The Fan Museum (The Fan Museum Trust). 12 Crooms Hill, Greenwich, London SE10 8ER
Tel: 020 8305 1441 or 020 8858 7879 Fax: 020 8293 1889

FASHION RESEARCH CENTRE

The Fashion Research Centre is an extension of the Museum of Costume, Bath, providing study facilities in the history of dress, housing a library and containing: books, periodicals, fashion magazines, and archival material. The study collection contains over 6000 examples of dress and accessories. Open by appointment.

Fashion Research Centre. 4 Circus, Bath BA1 2EW
Tel: 01225 477752 Fax: 01225 444793

THE FORGE MILL NEEDLE MUSEUM

An extensive range of hand and machine sewing needles in the museum shop available.

The Forge Mill Needle Museum. Needle Mill Lane, Riverside,
Redditch, Worcestershire B98 8HY
Tel: 01527 62509

GALLERY OF COSTUME

Costume museum and research centre housing an important collection of costume from 1600-1999. Dress displays of various periods and examples of knitting and crochet. Stored collections and use of reference library by appointment, housing fashion magazines, plates and shop catalogues. Gallery shop.

Gallery of Costume. Platt Hall, Rusholme, Manchester M14 5LL
Tel: 0161 224 5217 Fax: 0161 256 3278

HASTINGS EMBROIDERY

The 80 yard embroidery illustrates British history from 1066 to modern times, presenting 81 great events in British history from the Battle of Hastings up to modern times in full colour. Produced by the Royal School of Needlework, using threads, cords, fabrics, metals and jewels. Also a scale model of the Battle of Hastings and dolls in period costume.

Hastings Embroidery. Sussex Hall, White Rock Theatre, Hastings, East Sussex
Tel: 01424 781000 Fax: 01424 781170

HELMSHORE TEXTILE MUSEUMS

Two mill museums displaying many aspects of Lancashire's textile industry. One a woollen mill with working water wheel, the other a cotton mill where spinning mules are demonstrated daily.

Helmshore Textile Museums, Higher Mill Holcombe Road, Helmshore BB4 4NP
Tel: 01706 226459

THE FAN MUSEUM

This unique and award-winning museum is the only museum in the world dedicated to the history of fans, and the art and craft of fan-making. Housed in beautifully restored 18th century town houses in the centre of Historic Greenwich, The Fan Museum is home to an unsurpassed collection of over 3000 fans from around the world dating from the 11th century. Its own collections and fans lent from other collections are displayed in changing themed exhibitions.

Special guided tours may include elegantly served refreshments in the spectacular Orangery, with hand-painted murals and view over a Japanese inspired garden.

Gift shop. Special facilities including a lift and toilet are provided for the disabled. Close to BR, Greenwich Pier.

The museum is also available for private functions, product launches, corporate hospitality events...

Open: Tuesday to Saturday 11.00 am - 5pm, Sunday 12.00 noon - 5pm. Closed on Mondays (except bank holiday Mondays).

Admission charges: Adults: £3.50, Concessions: £2.50, Free on Tuesdays for Disabled and OAPs (except for groups) from 2pm.

For further information about our group tours, other activities or programme of exhibitions, please contact The Fan Museum, 12 Crooms Hill, Greenwich, London SE10 8ER. Tel: 0181 305 1441 or 0181 858 7879, Fax: 0181 293 1889

HITCHIN MUSEUM

Nineteenth century house showing permanent collection of costume depicting changes in womens fashions from 1830-1950, plus a large collection of archival material including mens, womens and childrens dress, accessories, footwear, bed linen etc. available to researchers by appointment.

Hitchin Museum. Paynes Park, Hitchin, Hertfordshire SG5 1EQ
Tel: 01462 434476 Fax: 01462 431316

HOLLYTREES MUSEUM

Georgian town house containing exhibits of costume, the Decorative Arts and social history.

Hollytrees Museum, High Street, Colchester, Essex CO1 1UG
Tel: 01206 282940

THE HUMPHRIES WEAVING COMPANY LTD

The last commercially operating hand loom silk weaver in England. Working silk museum.

**The Humphries Weaving Company Ltd. Devere Mill, Queen Street,
Castle Hedingham, Halstead, Essex CO9 3HA**
Tel: 01787 461193 Fax: 01787 462701

IMPERIAL WAR MUSEUM

Wealth of military reference material including large exhibition hall, art galleries, a shop and restaurant.

Imperial War Museum. Lambeth Road, London SE1 6H2
Tel: 020 7416 5000 Fax: 020 7416 5374

IRISH LINEN CENTRE & LISBURN MUSEUM

Working demonstrations "Living Looms" and hands-on-exhibition.

Irish Linen Centre & Lisburn Museum. Market Square, Lisburn, Co. Antrim BT28 1AG
Tel: 01846 663377 Fax: 01846 672624

JUDITH CLARK COSTUME GALLERY

Judith Clark Costume is a Gallery dedicated to the exhibition of fashion and historical costume, with a library in the basement (relevant books and catwalk slides) and a small bookshop.

Judith Clark Costume Gallery. 112 Talbot Road, London W11 1JR
Tel: 020 7727 2754 Fax: 020 7792 3573

THE LACE CENTRE

Exhibits include genuine Worthingham lace all locally made. Mail order available.

The Lace Centre. Severns Building, Castle Road, Nottingham NG1 6AA
Tel: 0115 941 3539

THE LACE MUSEUM & ART GALLERUY

Specialist collections of hats and lace from the eighteenth century to the twentieth century. Some items on public display, large study collections - available by appointment to individuals and groups.

The Lace Museum & Art Gallery. Wardown Park, Old Bedford Road, Luton LU2 7HA
Tel: 01582 546722/3

THE LEATHER CONSERVATION CENTRE

Conservation of leather objects of historic or artistic value. Publications on leather and its conservation. Dyes and surface coatings.

The Leather Conservation Centre. University College Campus, Boughton Green Road, Northampton NN2 7AN
Tel: 01604 719766 Fax: 01604 719649

LOTHERTON HALL

Costume and textile collection. Education room and workshops. Hall grounds include bird garden and deer park.

Lotherton Hall. Lotherton Lane, Aberford, Leeds LS25 3BD
Tel: 0113 281 3259

LUTON MUSEUM & ART GALLERY

Specialist collections of hats and lace from the eighteenth century to the twentieth century. Some items on public display, large study collections available by appointment to individuals and groups.

Luton Museum & Art Gallery. Wardown Park, Old Bedford Road, Luton LU2 7HA
Tel: 01582 546722/3

MACCLESFIELD SILK MUSEUM & HERITAGE CENTRE

Museum devoted to the history of the silk industry and Paradise Mill, home to 26 Jacquard silk handlooms. Guided tours, models of costume, displays and demonstrations of hand loom weaving. Silk shop selling extensive range of silk, silk products and a number of publications relating to silk.

Macclesfield Silk Museum & Heritage Centre. Roe Street, Macclesfield, Cheshire SK11 6UT
Tel: 01625 613210 Fax: 01625 617880

MUSEUM OF COSTUME

Extensive displays of fashionable dresses for men, women and children from late 16th Century to the present day.

Museum of Costume. Assembly Rooms, Bennett Street, Bath, Somerset BA1 2QH
Tel: 01225 477789 Fax: 01225 444793

MUSEUM OF COSTUME & TEXTILES

Extensive collection of costumes and embroideries dating from 1790 to the mid Twentieth Century, beautifully displayed in a series of atmospheric period rooms authentically furnished and decorated. Plus renowned lace collection relating to the Lace Industry of Nottingham

Museum of Costume & Textiles. Castle Gate, Nottingham NG1 6AF
Tel: 0115 915 3500 Fax: 0115 915 3653

MUSEUM OF JEWELLERY

Exhibits include the story of jewellery-making in Birmingham and contemporary jewellery design. A changing programme of exhibitions.

Jewellery Quarter Discovery Centre. 75-79 Vyse Street, Hockley, Birmingham, West Midlands B18 6HA
Tel: 0121 554 3598 Fax: 0121 554 3598

MUSEUM OF LEATHERCRAFT COLLECTION

Displays in leathercraft, gallery showing all aspects of leatherworking from gloves to blackjacks. Waterer-Spiers collection of modern leathercraft. Reserve collection and library available for study by appointment.

Museum of Leathercraft. Northampton Museums & Art Gallery, Guildhall Road, Northampton NN1 1DP
Tel: 01604 233500 ext 5104

MUSEUM OF LONDON

The largest city museum in the world, the Museum of London's collection illustrates London society and culture past and present. About 50 knitted items.

Museum of London. 150 London Wall, London EC2Y 5HN
Tel: 020 7600 3699 Fax: 020 7600 1058

MUSEUM OF NOTTINGHAM LACE

Lace museum with costumes, working machines, lace exhibits and audio tour of museum and Lace Market. Museum shop.

Museum of Nottingham Lace. 3-5 High Pavement, The Lace Market, Nottingham NG1 1HF
Tel: 0115 989 7365 Fax: 0115 989

MUSEUM OF SCIENCE & TECHNOLOGY IN MANCHESTER

The Museum of Science and Technology in Manchester has galleries that amuse, amaze and entertain from industry to interactives and sewers to space - a place of fascination.

Museum of Science and Technology in Manchester. Liverpool Road, Castlefield, Manchester M3 4FP
Tel: 0161 832 2244 Fax: 0161 833 2184

MUSEUM OF WELSH LIFE

Eighteenth Century working woollen mill in re-erected building, (part of 100 acre museum site). All woollen processes carried out using historic machinery, products for sale: blankets, shawls etc.

Museum of Welsh Life. St. Fagans, Cardiff CF5 6XB
Tel: 01222 5735000 Fax: 01222 573490

MUSEUM OF WELSH WOOLLEN INDUSTRY

Set in the heart of West Wales, amidst swiftly flowing streams, the museum tells the story of the most traditional of rural industries - Wool. Working wool museum.

Museum of Welsh Woollen Industry. Dre-fach Felindre, Llandysul, Carmarthenshire SA4 45UP
Tel: 01559 370929 Fax: 01559 371592

NATIONAL MUSEUMS OF SCOTLAND

Illustrated history of Scotland. Gallery of European costume from 1730 onwards to the present day.

National Museum of Scotland. Chambers Street, Edinburgh EG1 12F
Tel: 0131 225 7534 Fax: 0131 247 4070

NEWTOWN TEXTILE MUSEUM

Static exhibition of the woollen industry of the Newtown area. Four hand weaving looms and spinning wheels, explaining the processes from shearing through to weavng. Museum includes exhibits from other related industries.

Newtown Textile Museum. Commercial Street, Newtown, Powys, Wales
Tel: 01686 622024

NORTHAMPTON CENTRAL MUSEUM & ART GALLERY

The national collection of footwear containing over 10,000 shoes, machines, tools, trimmings and archive material. Permanent display and temporary exhibitions. Enquiries welcome. Study facilities available by appointment.

Northampton Central Museum & Art Gallery. Guildhall Road, Northampton NN1 1DP
Tel: 01604 238548 Fax: 01604 238720

NOTTINGHAM INDUSTRIAL MUSEUM

Eighteenth Century stables exhibiting the History of Nottingham Textile Industries. Collection of nationally important historic lace machines and locally made hosiery machinery. Hosiery, lace, printing and pharmacy.

Nottingham Industrial Museum. Courtyard Buildings, Wollaton Park, Nottingham, NG8 2AE
Tel: 0115 915 3910 Fax: 0115 915 3941

PAISLEY MUSEUM & ART GALLERIES

A world famous collection of Paisley shawls and many more origional pattern books. Resource for textile artists and designers. Contact: Keeper of Textiles.

Paisley Museum & Art Galleries. High Street, Paisley PA1 2BA
Tel: 0141 889 3151 Fax: 0141 889 9240

PARADISE MILL

Museum devoted to the history of the silk industry. Exhibits include: silk handlooms with Jacquard. Demonstrations of hand weaving, design and card cutting rooms. Gift shop.

Paradise Mill. Park Lane, Macclesfield SK11 6TJ
Tel: 01625 618228

PARKHAM ELIZABETHAN HOUSE & GARDENS

Elizabethan House-displaying an important collection of early needlework/tapestries.

Parkham Elizabethan House & Gardens. Parkham Park, Near Pulborough, West Sussex RH20 4HS
Tel: 01903 742021 Fax: 01903 746557

THE QUAKER TAPESTRY EXHIBITION

A visual chronicle of Quaker life, movement and its development throughout the centuries. Mail order throughout the year of unique items such as woollen embroidery cloth, 100% cotton woven in the museum, the stitch manual and the pictoral guide to the Quaker Tapestry, plus many more items. An educational list of publications available. Free mail order catalogue.

The Quaker Tapestry Exhibition. Friends' Meeting Place, Stramongate, Kendal, Cumbria LA9 4BH
Tel: 01539 722975

QUARRY BANK MILL TRUST (ENTERPRISES) LTD

Award winning Georgian cotton mill, and museum. A living, working museum, telling the story of King Cotton from bale of raw cotton to bolt of finished cotton.

Quarry Bank Mill Trust (Enterprises) Ltd. Quarry Bank Mill. Styal, Wilmslow, Cheshire SK9 4LA
Tel: 01625 527468 Fax: 01625 539267

RACHEL B. KAY SHUTTLEWORTH COLLECTION OF TEXTILES

Study facilities and specialist textile reference library.

Rachel B. Kay Shuttleworth Collection of Textiles. Gawthorpe Hall, Padiham, Nr. Burnley, Lancashire BB12 8UA

ROYAL CORNWALL MUSEUM

Collection of fashion, textiles, fabrics and fabric design.

Royal Cornwall Museum. River Street, Truro, Cornwall TR1 2SJ
Tel: 01872 272205

RUDDINGTON FRAMEWORK KNITTERS' MUSEUM

Unique surviving Victorian Knitters' yard, furnished cottages and frameshops around garden courtyard. Experience working and living conditions of the knitting community. Historic frames demonstrated, also Griswolds. A collection of handframes, which can be seen working daily. There is also a collection of circular sock machines.

Ruddington Framework Knitters' Museum. Chapel Street, Ruddington, Nottingham NG11 6HE
Tel: 0115 984 6914

SADDLEWORTH MUSEUM & ART GALLERY

Museum covering the history of textile production in Saddleworth area. Working machinery and demonstrations of textile processes. Extensive archive of textile company records. Cloth available to purchase.

Saddleworth Museum & Art Gallery. High Street, Uppermill, Nr. Oldham OL3 6HS
Tel: 01457 874093 Fax: 01457 870336

SALISBURY & SOUTH WILTSHIRE MUSEUM

The museums costume collection reflects the life and society of the region from silks of the rich to patchwork quilting, Dowton Lace attracting lacemakers' worldwide.

Salisbury & South Wiltshire Museum. The Kings House, 65 The Close, Salisbury, Wiltshire SP1 2EN
Tel: 01722 332151 Fax: 01722 325611

THE SALTER COLLECTION

Museum presenting costumes from 1785 to the 1950's.

The Salter Collection. 18 Gladstone Road, Deal, Kent CT14 7ET
Tel: 01304 361471

SCOTTISH TARTANS' MUSEUM

"Learn the facts, explore the history and discover the tartan"
Learn detailed accounts of historic Scotsmen and women from the development of the kilt to the present day. Audio guided facility in a selection of languages.

Scottish Tartans' Museum. The Scottish House. 39-41 Princes Street, Edinburgh, Scotland
Tel: 0131 556 1252 Fax: 0131 556 9529

SHAMBELLIE HOUSE MUSEUM OF COSTUME

Set in attractive wooded grounds, Shabellie House, a Victorian country house containing costumes from 1850's to 1920's, offering visitors the opportunity to view period clothing in appropriate room settings with accessories, furniture and Decorative Art.

Shambellie House Museum of Costume. New Abbey, Dumfries, Scotland DG2 8HQ
Tel: 01387 850375 Fax: 01387 850461

SHETLAND MUSEUM

Over 200 knitted items. Fair Isle knitting examples included.

Shetland Museum. Lower Hillhead, Lerwick, Shetland ZE1 2EL
Tel: 01595 695057 Fax: 01595 696729

SHUGBOROUGH HALL ESTATE

Costume department, spinning demonstrations and workshops.

Shugborough Hall Estate. Milford, Nr. Stafford ST17 0XB
Tel: 01889 881388

SILK MUSEUM & CRAFT WORKSHOP

Working mill and exhibition of the history of silk. Demonstrations of silk painting.

Silk Museum & Craft Workshop. David Evans & Company, Bourne Road, Crayford, Kent DA1 4BP
Tel: 01322 559401 Fax: 01322 550476

SILK MUSEUM

The history of the silk industry of Macclesfield cocoon to loom. Costumes, film and audio visual, displays include the social to the cultural history.

The Heritage Centre, Roe Street, Macclesfield SK11 6UT
Tel: 01625 613210 Fax: 01625 617880

SPRINGHILL COSTUME MUSEUM

A costume collection of around 3000 pieces, dating from the early Eighteenth Century to present day.

Springhill. Moneymore, Magherafelt, Co Londonderry BT45 7NQ
Tel/Fax: 01648 748210

STITCHES & LACE

Lace museum. Supplies for lacemaking, cross stitch, patchwork, quilting and tapestry.

Stitches & Lace. Alby Craft Centre, Cromer Road, Alby, Norwich, Norfolk NR11 7QE
Tel: 01263 768002

TEXTILE CONSERVATION CENTRE

Apartment 22, Hampton Court Palace, East Moseley, Surrey KT8 9AU
Tel: 020 8977 4943

THEATRE MUSEUM

Stage models, costumes, prints, posters, puppets, props and a variety of theatrical memorabilia, devoted to ballet, opera, dance, music hall and drama.

Theatre Museum. Russell Street, Covent Garden, London WC2
Tel: 020 7836 7891

TOTNES COSTUME MUSEUM

Devonshire collection of period costume. A themed annual exhibition of period costume displayed in Tudor merchants house.

Totnes Costume Museum. Bogan House, 43 High Street, Totnes, Devon TQ9 5NP
Tel: 01803 862857

THE ULSTER MUSEUM
NATIONAL MUSEUMS OF NORTHERN IRELAND

The costume and textile collection includes costume and accessories, Irish and continental lace, embroidery and household linens. An extensive collection of approximately 200 Mountmellick examples.

The Ulster Museum - The National Museum of Northern Ireland.
Botanic Gardens, Belfast, Northern Ireland BT9 5AB
Tel: 02890 383000 Fax: 02890 383003

VICTORIA & ALBERT MUSEUM

The V & A holds one of the world's largest and most diverse collections of the Decorative Arts, housed in magnificent Victorian buildings. 146 galleries contain unrivalled collections dating from 3000 BC to the present day, spanning 2000 years of art and design around the world. The permanent fashion collection ranges from eighteenth century court dress to clothes of the nineteen nineties New Age Travellers.

Victoria & Albert Museum. Cromwell Road, South Kensington, London SW7 2RL
Tel: 020 7938 8500 Fax: 020 7938 8341

THE WANDLE INDUSTRIAL MUSEUM

The museum pays homage to Morris and Liberty, having a collection of Liberty and Morris textiles, hand printed blocks and silk screens. Research facilities available.

The Wandle Industrial Museum. The Vestry Hall Annexe, London Road, Mitcham, Surrey CR4 3UD
Tel: 020 8648 0127 Fax: 020 8685 0249

THE WEAVERS' COTTAGES MUSEUM

18th Century craftsman's house containing traditional weaving exhibits.

The Weavers' Cottages Museum. 23-27 Wellwynd, Airdrie ML6 OBN
Tel: 01236 747712

THE WILLIAM MORRIS GALLERY

Set in the historic Georgian house, Morris's family home from 1848 to 1856, the William Morris Gallery details Morris's life, work and influence.

The William Morris Gallery. Lloyd Park, Forest Road, London E17 4PP
Tel: 020 8527 3782

WIMBLEDON LAWN TENNIS MUSEUM

The history of lawn tennis. Exhibits include: fashion, costume and memorabilia.

Wimbledon Lawn Tennis Museum. All England Club, Church Road, Wimbledon SW19 5AE
Tel: 020 8946 6131 Fax: 020 8944 6497

WORKING SILK MUSEUM

Heirloom silk weavers. Visit to see how silk fabrics are produced from the raw material to the finished cloth. Textiles and mill shop. Books, leaflets, posters, samples, cocoons etc. all available by mail order.

Working Silk Museum. New Mills, South Street, Baintree, Essex. CM7 3GB
Tel: 01376 553393 Fax: 01376 330642

WYGSTON'S HOUSE MUSEUM OF COSTUME

Late Medieval building, housing costume from 1850 to present day. Reconstruction of draper's dress shop of 1920's, Hat Gallery and changing programme of fashion.

Wygston's House Museum of Costume. Wygston House. 12 Applegate, St Nicholas Circle, Leicester LS1 5LD
Tel: 0116 247 3056 Fax: 0116 262 0964

YORK CASTLE MUSEUM

Hand and machine knitting including 200 knitted articles.

York Castle Museum. The Eye of York, York YO1 1RY
Tel: 01904 653611 Fax: 01904 671078

ARTS COUNCIL FOR WALES
Holst House. 9 Museum Place, Cardiff CF1 3NX
Tel: 01222 349711 Fax: 01222 221447

ARTS COUNCIL OF ENGLAND
14 Great Peter Street, London SW1P 3NQ
Tel: 0171 333 0100 Fax: 0171 973 6590

ARTS COUNCIL OF GREAT BRITAIN
105 Piccadily, London W1V OAU

ARTS COUNCIL OF IRELAND
70 Merrion Square, Dublin 2, Eire
Tel: 00 353 661 1840

ARTS COUNCIL OF NORTHERN IRELAND
Mac Neice House, 77 Malone Road, Belfast BT9 6AQ

ARTS COUNCIL OF WALES CRAFT DEPARTMENT
9 Museum Place, Cardiff, South Glamorgan CF1 3NX
Tel: 01222 376500

CRAFTS COUNCIL OF IRELAND
Castle Yard, Kilkenny, Eire
Tel: 00353 1 679 7383

EASTERN ARTS BOARD
Eastern Arts Board. Cherry Hinton Hall, Cambridge CB1 4DW
Tel: 01223 215355

EAST MIDLANDS ARTS
Regional Arts Board serving Derbyshire, Leicestershire, Lincolnshire, Northamptonshire, Nottinghamshire and Rutland, promoting the arts, supporting professional artists, overseas goverment and lottery funding within the arts sector.
East Midlands Arts. Mountfields House, Epinal Way, Loughborough LE11 0QE
Tel: 01509 218292 Fax: 01509 262214

LONDON ARTS BOARD
London Arts Board is the arts funding and development agency for the capital. It promotes excellence and innovation in the arts throughout London.
London Arts Board. Elm House, 133 Long Acre, London WC2E 9AF
Tel: 020 7240 1313 Fax: 020 7670 2400

NORTHERN ARTS

Regional Arts Board for Cumbria, Durham, Northumberland, Teeside, Tyne and Wear.

Northern Arts. 9-10 Osborne Terrace, Jesmond, Newcastle upon Tyne NE2 5AB
Tel: 0191 281 6334 Fax: 0191 281 3276

NORTH WEST ARTS BOARD

Manchester House, 22 Bridge Street, Manchester M3 AB
Tel: 0161 834 6644

SCOTTISH ARTS COUNCIL

12 Manor Place, Edinburgh EH3 7DD
Tel: 0131 243 2437

SOUTHERN ARTS

13 St Clement Street, Winchester S023 9DQ
Tel: 01962 855099

SOUTHERN EAST ARTS BOARD

10 Mount Ephrain, Tunbridge Wells TN4 8AS

SOUTHERN WEST ARTS

Bradnich Place, Gandy Street, Exeter, Devon EX4 3LS
Tel: 01392 218188 Fax: 01392 413557

WELSH ARTS COUNCIL

Holst House, Museum Place, Cardiff CF1 3NX

WEST MIDLANDS ARTS

82 Granville Street, Birmingham B1 2LH
Tel: 0121 631 3121

YORKSHIRE & HUMBERSIDE ARTS

21 Bond Street, Dewsbury, West Yorkshire WF13 1AX
Tel: 01924 455555

WALES CRAFTS COUNCIL

Hanfaes Lane, Welshpool, Powys SY21 7BE
Tel: 01938 555313 Fax: 01938 556237ì

MUSEUMS & RESEARCH CENTRES

OTHER USEFUL ADDRESSES

USEFUL BUSINESS ADDRESSES

DESIGN CO-ORDINATORS
CAROL MARY BROWN

JOHN SKINNER

COVER CONCEPT
ANNA TRYNTJA

JIM COUNSELL

TREND DIRECTIONS

KATE HENDERSON

EDITORIAL
GEORGE W. BROWN

CONTRIBUTORS
GEORGE BROWN

DIANA BUXTON

JULIAN BERWICK

ANNA TRYNTJA

TYPESET /DESIGNERS
TYPETEC, COUNTY HALL, MARKET PLACE, BOSTON, LINCOLNSHIRE PE21 6DY
TEL: 01205 369560 FAX: 01205 369561

PRINTED BY
CLASSIC PRINTERS

ADVERTISING
JOHN SKINNER